ANYONE CAN FLY

In the gray half-light of dawn, the uncertain groaning whine of a cold engine . . . its sudden ear-crushing roar firing-up . . . the subdued shriek of jets overhead in the blackness of midnight . . . the comforting screech-plunk of tires firmly glued onto a runway . . . the lost airstrip in the rain and haze: these are the unforgettable sounds and images of the air age – the fabric of which we are the weavers and the woven – of mankind discovering his wings even as he launches far out of his own world. . . .

ANYONE CAN FLY

JULES BERGMAN

DOUBLEDAY & COMPANY, INC.
GARDEN CITY, NEW YORK, 1964

PHOTO CREDITS

The Port Authority of New York, 12, 75, 76, 79
Mobil Oil, 128–29
Gordon Vincent of Lock Haven, Pennsylvania, 30, 41–44, 61–70, 78, 88, 90–92, 106, 119, 134, 159, 164–66, 169
Fairchild Aerial Survey, Inc., 127–28
World-Telegram and Sun, photo by Herman Hiller, 176
Donald Summers, Ridgewood News Photo, 177, 180, 182
Cessna Aircraft Co., 183, 211–24
Beech Aircraft Corporation, 184, 185, 197–205
Dimstt Brothers, 185
James Laughead, 187, 188
Martin and Keiman, 187
Piper Aircraft Corporation, 188, 191–96
Mooney Aircraft Corporation, 206–7
All other pictures by the author

Library of Congress Catalog Card Number 64–10558
Copyright © 1964 by Jules Bergman. All Rights Reserved
Printed in the United States of America
First Edition

TURBULENCE

Let not the air conquer us,
Let us conquer it!
Let not the darkness envelop us, rather
Let us seek its hidden pathways
Falling not through the hidden traps of the air forest
Scraped not by the harsh blows of secreted limbs
Cooled here in the moist crevasses of the winged soul.
Let us seek solitude, not agreers;
Light, not the darkness of many companies;
Certitude, not Confusion;
Correctness, not Compliance.
Let us steer by men, not stars
Reckon by the trembling of our wings,
Not by what others say.
And when darkness looms uncertain,
When hail smashes at the windshield
Of our winged souls
Let us rejoice! Let us take heart
From the harshness, the cruelty of
What we have made.
Would that we forever had the strength to endure
The crosswinds of circumstance,
The unexpected gust at noon as well
As at midnight.
Else how would we have known
The adventure we sought and whether
We were conqueror or conquered . . .

                                              J.B.

CONTENTS

SELECTED LIST OF ILLUSTRATIONS

PREFACE

This is a book about learning to fly, not a book that will teach you how to fly. No book will: only in doing it will you learn, though books will help you understand how. In this book we hope to impart the adventure, the fun and much of the doing—enough so that, having read it, you will be able to begin flying knowing the basics and thoroughly familiar with the language and the habits of the air.

Linking picture-and-words with aerial maneuvers depicted from inside and outside the cockpit, we think, may have supplied much of the missing visual link so invaluable in understanding the art and the science of flying.

We have sought to weave into this story the saga of private flying in the United States—a tale that has hardly begun and one whose future is almost limitless. We would offer thanks and praise to the tireless, sky-loving instructors who are the flesh-and-blood embodiment of the continuity that is enabling general aviation to grow.

Special thanks and praise are due to:

The men of the Federal Aviation Agency's Flight Service Stations and Air Traffic Control Centers who, laboring under immense obstacles, have made America's skies the safest in the world.

Bill Robinson of Cessna Aircraft, and Bill Strohmeier and Piper Aircraft Company, for advice and technical assistance.

My wife, Joanne, who typed, researched, encouraged, learned to fly herself, has since co-piloted us, and in the process, pioneered a navigational system that remains a deep mystery, though it always works.

Last and first, may we humbly point to the brothers Wright of Dayton, Ohio, as well as the creative dreamers who preceded them and in many ways are responsible for the birth of the entire project.

JULES BERGMAN
Pomona, New York – 1964

ANYONE CAN FLY

Manhattan's towers, eight miles in the distance, are a dramatic background for Teterboro Airport, one of the busiest private- and business-plane fields in the nation.

Chapter One. DISCOVERY

Looking down, as the runway disappears in a blur behind you, and the world below suddenly grows smaller, you'll find this moment of truth, your first flight, almost unbelievable. Yet, it all rings true: unlike being in an airliner, you and the airplane are *one,* you are part of what happens, and you're discovering not only why and how it happens, but the even more satisfying truth that you *make* it happen.

As your plane banks away from the airport and climbs higher, and your doubts begin to disappear, you'll probably look backward on the weeks and months you waited before first taking up flying. Like untold thousands who quested the sky, you dreamed and planned it for years. It will have been a game, with and without words, played each time an airplane engine reverberated in your ears and stirred your spirit. Now, looking down on the cars crawling beneath your plane, you'll think back to traffic jams *you* were trapped in, when you closed your eyes and prayed silently to be able to *fly* over the endless lines of cars—until the auto behind you shattered the dream. Or, picking out a plane in the sky making its way home at dusk, you may have craved the adventure, dreamed that you were in it, headed away from the everyday. And it was doubtless an unfulfilled dream for a long time.

Flying will enable you to get far away on weekends, much farther than in a car. Yet you'll sense that this cannot be the complete reason why you do it. It is adventure you wanted as well, the lure of being in a new dimension. And a desire to be on your own, which few of us, surrounded in this crowded society by our fellow men, manage to achieve. It is all of these things and something else, something much deeper, which few can adequately put into words. Few flyers can. For, as you'll see, you *live* the answer.

"Why?" you'll have asked yourself dozens of times. "Why do I *have* to fly?" And you'll find many, many answers on your first and on later flights: to escape the pressures of your office or job; to get away from people, phones and everyday problems; to forget the demands of our existence. All of us have a different, deeply personal reason, but it nearly always is tied in with getting away from the crushing, ceaseless cycle of twentieth-century life, getting away and doing something different. Something different, trying (at first), yet deeply satisfying and relaxing at the same time. It is a deep inner emotion experienced at the exact instant of a plane's lifting off the runway. It is man overcoming his own disbelief as he discovers he *can* be airborne.

A simple, small thing, yet even in this sophisticated space age it goes far toward explaining the mystique of flying. It is basic. And that first day at the airport watching the procession of planes cracking ground, you'll feel it run through you, if it doesn't put itself into words. Hopefully, it'll resolve many of your inner doubts and reassure you that you *do* belong, for that first day will seem pretty strange.

You will notice that the people at the airport all seem to speak a different language, casually dropping phrases like "sucker holes," "ceilings," "quartering tail winds" and "omni." You'll feel a little like Charlie Chaplin stumbling with pails and mops at a bankers' convention. You'll say as little as possible because each time you ask anything everyone looks up helpfully to answer your question and you may feel doubly foolish.

Another rather puzzling thing will be that none of the people look very much like what you had figured fliers *should* look like. None of them have the gaunt, strained look of the old-time stick-and-rudder men; nor do they have the devil-may-care abandon of Hollywood's portrayal of pilots; and they most certainly aren't the glossy stereotypes of the cigaret ads. It is pretty disconcerting—they look like *people,* not fliers. Some are tall, some short, some in between. Most are neatly-dressed average types you might find anywhere. They talk rather earnestly among themselves, thrashing out problems, but always in a casual, undramatic manner, behavior not in keeping with the general image of the pilot. All of this, of course, serves only to further add to the confusion of the beginner. Don't let it bother you. Your doubts will end quickly enough as the instructor, assigned to you by the flying school, motions you out of the Operations Building and out onto the field. He too may seem just a bit strange at first.

He might have been expected to be wearing the battered Air Force leather flying jacket, khaki shirt and wrinkled suntans that fliers always wear in stories. In reality, he'll probably be wearing a neat sports jacket, slacks, shirt and tie. For most instructors these days are part of flying's new image of respectability, an outgrowth of this era of businessmen fliers, who frequently take along an instructor to get in flying time and work in a lesson on the way to and from an appointment in a city hundreds of miles distant.

The new breed of instructor these days debunks the perpetual Hollywood portrait of the madcap pilot. The helmet and goggles went out with biplanes, and the leather jackets with the Flying Tigers. Even the Air Force nowadays uses neat green nylon flight jackets.

In today's comfortable enclosed-cabin private planes, flight jackets linger on to be worn on blustery days or on long cross-country hops, but for most flying they are an affectation rather than a necessity.

Parked on the grass, its wings and tail anchored with ropes, sits the airplane that will become your home in the air. It's probably one of the newer tricycle gear ships—the Cessna 150 or 172, the Piper Cherokee or Tri-Pacer, or the Beech Musketeer. The addition of that third or nose wheel to the conventional two-wheeled planes of the past overnight made learning to fly nearly twice as easy. The plane will be brightly two- or three-toned and perhaps look brave and frail all at once, much as you may feel during your first session.

The instructor motions you to follow him around the plane in a walk-around inspection (just as it's done on airliners) while he explains how and why it flies

—how wings, ailerons, elevator and rudder work. He'll open the engine cowling and show you what the power plant looks like, check the oil level, close and lock the cowling tightly and then invite you to get in.

And that will be your next surprise. The plane is upholstered much like any new car, with clean, neat vinyl and leather upholstery. That will strike you immediately, once you are inside it: the plane seems like a familiar symbol; it has even been finished on the inside like a car itself, one of the most everyday symbols imaginable. The seats are deep and comfortable, if somewhat cramped; two in front, two more in back with a sizable luggage compartment behind the rear seat.

If you are the suspicious type, you may search for parachutes. They aren't there. You don't need them. In the unlikely event the engine should fail, you can glide to an airport or a highway and put down safely. Most light planes have a nine-to-one glide ratio: when you're one mile up—5280 feet—you can glide nine miles, and, if you're careful and use your training, that should be plenty of room to find a safe landing spot.

The instructor will lecture you briefly on the wheel and rudder and how they control the airplane, show you how to use the throttle, and then will go over the instruments. There are generally three rows of them, triple-banked on the dashboard, and they look as complicated as the control console in a blockhouse at Cape Kennedy. After the bare few instruments we're all used to on the dashboard of a car, it may look hopeless. But in a few minutes you'll begin to grasp how they work together to show you not only how the plane is flying, but how it should be flown.

The dashboard of Tri-Pacer Triple Two Delta. If it looks complicated, it *is*—until you get used to all the instruments.

Now comes a delicate moment. "All right," the instructor will say calmly, "let's go." An uncertainty, verging on fear or on delightful anticipation, will take place. You may feel trapped and want out, or you may be a "tiger," ready to go.

The instructor gives you a short briefing: "Now follow me on the controls, watch what I do, and if I tell you to let go, don't argue with me—let go!" You'll probably find yourself assuring him that you won't argue with him.

"Clear!" he shouts. Watching your puzzlement, he explains that you always look on all sides to be certain no one is in front of or even near the propeller *before* starting the engine. Then you shout "clear" to warn anyone who might be approaching.

He turns the key in the ignition, presses the starter button, and the propeller quickly spins around as the engine roars into life. Or, it *looks* like that was all he did. Actually, he also pushed the mixture control knob in to full rich, primed the engine with another push-pull knob, and turned on the master switch. But these are incidentals he may not bother setting you straight on the first time around. This is a first ride—to show you what the plane can do, and to see how you like it.

The plane begins to roll toward the taxiway. The instructor turns on the radio, speaks into a microphone by depressing a button, and a voice in the control tower (if your field has one) spiels a jumble of figures and directions—they seem meaningless. You are quite properly puzzled and apprehensive.

"Now," he declares, "here's what it means: altimeter setting '30 point 12'— that's the barometer reading—same as you hear on the radio. It governs the height setting on your altimeter. Altitude usually differs at every airport, and you have to set your altimeter correctly so as to gauge the plane's height as you land. It should *always* read the altitude of the field before takeoff. Next—wind southwest at 15 miles per hour. That means the wind is blowing *from* the southwest at

"Triple Two Delta ready to roll . . ."

15 miles per hour. And runway 24—that points to the southwest. You always take off and land *into* the wind; it helps you get off sooner at a safer, slower ground speed and lets you land more slowly. And you couldn't very well land with a tail wind—it would push the plane, making it hard to stop. Remember that the runway number is a compass setting—just add a zero. 24 is 240°, pointing southwest . . . 360° is north, 90° is east, 180° south and 270° west."

Other planes line up on the taxiway ahead of your ship. "While you wait for the other ships to get off," the instructor tells you, "you do a cockpit check and run-up."

This is a "following-through" procedure—checking out each instrument in a careful ritual (most planes now have printed takeoff and landing check lists on the dashboard) to be sure it is working correctly, and that the engine and controls on the plane are behaving properly. Then the instructor will put on the brake tightly and shove the throttle in to begin the run-up. The ignition key turns deftly in his hand. "There are two magnetos or electrical systems in the engine," he points out, "to be sure the ignition is always firing the engine. Cars only have one. We make sure *both* are working fully. Then carburetor heat"—he pulls out a little knob—"that burns out any ice in the engine in damp weather. Everything checks out."

Next, the instructor picks up the microphone, presses the button and says professionally, "Tri-Pacer Triple Two Delta—holding runway 24—ready to go.

"Always identify yourself—say where you are on the field and tell the tower when you're set to go. You use the last numbers and letter of the plane's identification, N7222D. The letter D is for Delta from the international aviation code." The voice in the tower again emerges from the speaker above you, as mysterious as before, uttering a crisp command this time.

"Tri-Pacer Triple Two Delta—cleared for takeoff." Taxiing out to the edge of runway 24, the plane turns onto the white center line.

The throttle is pushed full-in steadily, *smoothly*—not suddenly—and the plane trembles briefly with its unharnessed power and begins to roll down the runway. It doesn't jerk with its new-found speed like a car, but picks up momentum easily. Now the control wheel comes backward slowly and the plane fairly jumps into the air.

Triple Two Delta breaking ground, ready to fly . . .

Only a few seconds have passed, you've used no more than four hundred or five hundred feet of runway. Then, spellbound, you feel the wheels leave the blacktop of the runway as the plane lifts up and away. You are airborne.

This frail concoction of tubing, fabric or metal and engine, helpless on the ground, is in the air, in its own dimension, and it has suddenly grown tremendously in your eyes. It has become an airplane. It lifts off quickly and the ground drops away. There was little sensation, other than the reassuring roar of the engine and faint noise of air slipping past the wings and fuselage.

The instructor turns the wheel to the left, and the plane moves over to the left smoothly, as you clear the traffic pattern of the airport. Your stomach drops with the sudden, unexpected motion, then quickly comes back to normal as the wheel is turned to the right—coming back to straight-and-level flight. The instructor looks over at your anxious face, catches the panicky look midway into the turn and smiles reassuringly. "Don't worry. Next time you won't even notice it."

Turning away from the field after takeoff . . .

Discovery: the unfettered sense of freedom – independence from a world we depend on . . .

Looking down, you watch the ground slipping past. Thousands of houses, now shrunk to cheesebox dimensions, are spread out below. Cars have become toys, cramped together on thin white ribbons, choking each other. The world's shape, size and proportions have abruptly changed in a few seconds. You have found a world all of your own, above the tight, noisy jungle below. Now you know why you *had* to fly.

This is the first wild euphoria—the unfettered sense of freedom—the independence from a world we all depend on, yet want to, and need to, get away from.

The Tri-Pacer soars upward, passing 4000 feet, and it heads north away from the field. To the east, a jet flies high, winging toward the coast. Next, the instructor gives you a demonstration of a few basic turns—just enough to show you what the plane can do. Then you bank and glide down toward the field for a few minutes, the engine muted, lost in a rhapsody with the wind noise, and the sky blue above you.

Suddenly, you realize that the pressing worries of a seven-day-a-week life as an earth person have passed . . . left behind on the runway . . . forgotten in a twinkling in the concentrated exhilaration of your totally new experience. You've discovered a winged world.

Lost in the act of watching the Tri-Pacer fly itself, you are soon back over the airport. The radio crackles as the tower gives landing instructions. The sky is alive with many-colored small planes jockeying in the pattern for a landing. You take your place behind other planes flying *downwind* . . . with the wind *behind* . . . paralleling the runway for landing. Then base leg—a 90° turn until you cross a line perpendicular to the runway. Then the final approach, gliding in for a landing. The wheels touch smoothly with a faint screech of rubber. The first landing. You may be exhausted with the adventure or plain exhilarated with the realization of finally having flown. Perhaps you will be relieved to be on the ground and a little weak in the knees from memories. The ground feels good but the sky still seems to beckon, to say "come back," and you know you will.

And somehow, in half an hour, a transformation has taken place: no longer manacled to the earth, you have found a new land—an airborne universe—a secret place away from the everyday.

To each of us, flying has a different meaning—varied emotional shadings and feelings—but all of us have joined the secret society of fledgling birdmen.

You are flying.

Now you are one of us.

Chapter Two. WINGED WORLD: WHY THE AIRPLANE FLIES

Ask most men why an airplane flies and they will likely answer: "Anybody knows that!" Then they'll pretend to be shocked by *your* ignorance in not knowing. Press the question home and they will mutter some mumbo jumbo about lift, or the engine does it, and change the subject as swiftly as possible. Ask a small boy why an airplane flies and the odds are pretty good that he'll answer that the airplane *floats* on air. The instinctive answer is the right one. An airplane *does* float on air; we can see that. The question is: *Why* does it float on air?

The pressure exerted by our atmosphere, the same thing that makes a barometer work, is what enables winged flight in this world to be possible. The wing of the airplane puts atmospheric pressure to work and enables the airplane to fly. And the engine gives the airplane the ability to get off the ground and to fly where the pilot wants it to go without seeking upward air currents, which a glider uses.

Air is so light and so unnoticeable that we seldom realize it has weight or exerts pressure. Yet, at sea level, air exerts a pressure upon everything around it of about one ton per square foot. Air fills the earth's airspace to an altitude of hundreds of miles, and remains in a relatively balanced state. But let that balance be upset (and scientists are still searching for all the reasons *why* it gets disturbed) and the power of plain old air becomes devastating. Whatever the reason, air will move from high-pressure areas toward areas of lower pressure, and energy (wind) will be created. The result is impressively demonstrated with distressing regularity in hurricanes and storms. The energy potential of air is tapped in much the same way by an airplane's wing. When an airplane begins to move on the ground (driven forward by the thrust of its engine), the air balance is upset. The shape of the wing (or airfoil) creates a low-pressure area *above* the wing and a high-pressure area *under* it. The higher-pressure area under the wing seeks to move upward toward the low-pressure area. But the wing is in the way. So air under the wing *pushes* upward on the wing, creating energy or lift. If a wing is big enough and the airplane light enough it can fly without an engine; it becomes a glider.

For an airplane to develop enough lift, the wing has to be pushed or pulled through the air at a fairly good speed by the engine. The faster a wing moves the more lift it develops. And then, when the lift of the wing is greater than the

Ask a small boy why an airplane flies — he *knows*. . . .

weight of the airplane and the pull of gravity, the instant of magic takes place: the airplane becomes airborne. It takes off or, as some manuals still prefer to say, it *lifts* off.

THE FOUR FORCES OF FLIGHT

While lift can be regarded as the single most vital force in flight, there are three others just as important. The wing and its lift offset the second force—gravity—which tries to keep airplanes on the ground. The engine supplies the third force—thrust—which drives the plane forward through the air. And the air itself creates the fourth force—drag, or air resistance—which tries to hold the plane back from moving forward.

Probably the second most confusing term in aviation is *angle of attack*. Most people seem to think this has something to do with the fighter pilots who go after an enemy intruder lurking in the sun. Naturally, the romantic picture is incorrect, but the term does deal with attack—the way the wing attacks the air it slices through in its forward movement. Picture the flat underside of a wing. A straight line running from the front of the wing to its back is called the chord. The wing is designed to angle up into the air ever so slightly. The angle at which it bites or cuts into the air is called the angle of attack. It governs just how much lift a wing

Why an airplane flies. . . .

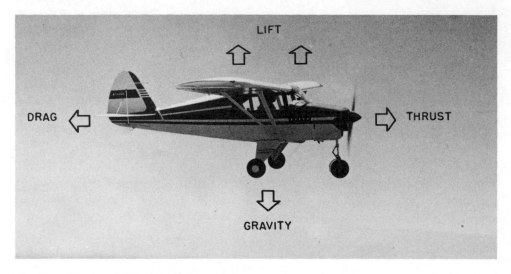

The Four Forces of Flight. . . .

can develop. And naturally the angle of attack changes as the airplane itself changes from climb to level flight and then descends.

The smaller the angle—or the less the wing is inclined—the less lift. As the wing rotates or turns upward and the angle increases, the amount of lift increases *up to a certain point*. Most airplanes stop developing lift after the angle of attack gets beyond about 20°. Beyond this, the lift abruptly falls off. The reason: after the upper wing surface has been angled too high, the air no longer flows smoothly over it—a burble of turbulence springs up—and lift begins to fall off rapidly. When this happens, the airplane is beginning to enter a stall. Simply and clearly stated, a stall is the critical airspeed at which a plane's wings can no longer support its own weight in the air. A stall has nothing to do with the engine conking out, or loss of power—it is loss of *airspeed*. And below this critical airspeed—*the stalling speed*—the plane is no longer properly controllable.

As soon as the wing's lift no longer can offset the plane's weight, it stalls in a
hurry and it's time to make a rapid recovery or trouble will result. A stall can
lead to a hurried and often unpleasantly final encounter with the ground in the
form of a spin or spiral. Today's highly stable airplanes resist the maneuver
staunchly. But it is possible to get into a stall if you're careless, which is why
it is vital to learn to recognize the conditions leading up to a stall.

More on this later. Just don't let stall get to be a frightening word; when an
airplane is landed well (we'll go over this later), it actually is stalled gently—
scant inches off the ground.

Another point about angle of attack: it can create drag as well as destroy lift.
As the angle of attack gets to be too great, air resistance builds up around the
wing and drag begins to work on the airplane. In the air it feels just like it looks
and sounds: the airplane is being *pulled* down toward the ground. The plane
will feel like it is mushing downward.

ANGLE OF ATTACK

Angle of attack: the angle at which the wing slices into, or *attacks,* the air to create lift.

THE FIVE CONTROLS OF AN AIRPLANE

Any self-respecting airplane is maneuvered on the ground and in the air by five basic controls:

1. *The elevator*. Hinged to the tail, its upward and downward motion controls the angle of attack of the airplane, and thus imparts to the plane upward and downward motion.
2. *The ailerons*. Hinged to the rear of the wing on its outward sides, the ailerons give the airplane its basic ability to turn in flight.
3. *The rudder*. Vertically hinged to the tail of the plane, it controls the direction of the airplane's nose, invaluably assisting the ailerons in making clean turns and giving the pilot directional control.
4. *The throttle*. The throttle, which controls the engine's power, gives the plane the proper amount of energy for takeoff, cruising flight, maneuvering, or *gaining or losing altitude*.
5. *The flaps*. The flaps are really invaluable auxiliary controls mounted inboard of the ailerons on the trailing edge of the wing. Their basic purpose is to increase the rate of descent with no increase in forward speed. They supply some increase in lift and a tremendous increase in drag. So flaps allow you to land more slowly (hence easily), to takeoff in less distance, and thus give you better control of the plane. Most have flaps.

THE ELEVATORS

Horizontally hinged to the tail, the elevators—moving up or down—control the pitch or up-and-down attitude of the airplane. Simply put, they seem to make the plane move up or down. Much more, of course, is involved: moving the elevators up or down pitches the nose—and the airplane itself—up or down, and changes the angle of attack of the wings because the wings themselves, being attached to the plane, move with it. The angle of attack is a function of the throttle as well as of the elevators. Think of it in these terms: the elevators control the pitch or up-and-down movement of the plane, the throttle controls airspeed and supplies power for climbing. Even simpler, the throttle controls your *altitude,* the elevators direct the plane up or down.

Rear view of elevators in "up" position.

Elevators: in "up" position.

Elevators: in "neutral" position.

Elevators: in "down" position.

The elevators are linked to the control wheel or stick by cables and pulleys. When you pull back on the wheel for takeoff or to climb, the elevator is forced upward as in picture ⌀13. The wind hits the elevator surface as it faces upward, and this *forces the tail down*. As the tail goes downward, the nose is forced upward. The wing's angle of attack increases and the airplane climbs, *if it has sufficient airspeed*. If it does not, the nose will still go upward, but the plane will mush and stall. Now when you push forward on the control wheel, the elevator moves downward, as in picture ⌀15, and the tail is *raised upward,* as the tail moves upward, the nose is directed down, the angle of attack lessens or ceases and the airplane descends.

The all-important point to learn here is never to think of the elevator as the device that makes the plane gain or lose altitude. The throttle is the device controlling climbing or descending. As we have seen, you can pull back on the elevator and the plane will not climb, even though the nose points skyward. If you continue to pull back on the elevators not only will the plane not climb, but it will descend more rapidly because you've raised the angle of attack beyond its effective point and destroyed the plane's lift.

The rule, we find, then is: the elevator controls the pitch *attitude* of the plane, the throttle governs the climbing power or the altitude of the plane.

THE AILERONS

As the steering wheel controls the turn of a car, so the aileron wheel controls the turn of an airplane *in the air*. On the ground, the rudder turns the airplane unless it has a steerable nose wheel (as most newer tri-gear planes do). Turning the aileron wheel, which seems like a car-type action, is in fact the motion that makes you feel that the cockpit does have some resemblance to an auto's front seat. Whereas turning the car's steering wheel actuates the front tires to enable the auto to turn, turning the aileron wheel actuates the ailerons enabling the plane to turn.

What the ailerons really do is tilt one wing so that the plane turns. A left-hand turn of the control wheel or stick makes the plane turn left; a right-hand motion moves the plane to the right. When you move the wheel to the left, the aileron in the left wing swings upward, as in picture ⌀17, *reducing* the effective lift of the wing, while at the same time, the right aileron moves downward, *increasing* the lift of the right airfoil. What happens is that the right wing then swings upward, while the left wing banks down, so that the plane swings to the left—into a left turn. The aileron movement has changed the forward vertical lift of the wing and swung the ship around to the left.

In a right turn, the same thing happens in reverse: the right aileron moves upward—the right wing loses lift—while the left aileron swings downward, increasing lift on the left wing, so that the plane banks to the right. But you also use the rudder to enter and exit from the turn to make it smoother and to be sure that the plane doesn't slip or skid. In a slip, the plane's nose is headed away from its true direction; in a skid, the plane literally is skidding: it is turning, but unevenly, skidding through the sky, instead of maneuvering smoothly.

The ailerons as positioned in a left turn; left aileron is up, right is down.

In a right turn, the right aileron moves up and the left down.

THE RUDDER

Just as the rudder of a ship, projecting downward into the sea, governs the direction of the ship's bow, so the rudder of an airplane projecting vertically upward into the air governs the direction of the airplane's nose. What really happens is that the rudder in both cases turns the stern or tail of the vehicle and forces the bow or nose to the desired direction. But add the extra dimension of an aircraft and the rudder alone is insufficient to turn the aircraft. The rudder therefore works *with* ailerons. Its basic purpose is to assist the ailerons as they do the primary job of turning the plane. Entering a turn, rudder is coordinated with aileron. Left aileron, left rudder; right aileron, right rudder; and once you have discovered the proper amount of rudder needed, the plane enters and recovers from the turn cleanly. The rudder is invaluable for precise directional control. Small course changes are better made with rudder than aileron.

When you push the left rudder pedal, the rudder swings left, forcing the tail to the right, which then swings the nose to the left. The right rudder pedal moves the rudder right and the airplane's nose to the right. But like anything else, the rudder is to be used with moderation. A sudden jab of rudder during a bank or a

For a right turn, the right rudder pedal moves the rudder to the right.

The rudder, positioned for a left turn.

turn can throw the airplane into a highly uncomfortable and possibly dangerous skid or even a spin.

The only place where the rudder does not work with the ailerons is in steering on the ground. There, like the rudder on a ship, it does the whole job (aided in most new planes by a steerable nose wheel).

THE FLAPS

Moving from its neutral or centered position to full down attitude, the flap changes the lifting area and shape of the wing. The more lift, the less drag; the airplane can take off or land more slowly, and thus can get out of or into a smaller landing field more readily and with less wearing-out of brakes and tires.

But the lift gained from use of the flaps increases the plane's drag, meaning that the speed of the airplane is lowered. So flaps are used entirely for landing or takeoff, never at cruising speed. As a matter of fact, you are specifically warned against using the flaps in most planes at full speed. Lowering them into the airstream at full speed can cause serious structural damage to the flaps. For example, in the Tri-Pacer, which has two notches of flaps—20° and 40°—use of any flap is prohibited at more than 100 mph. The first notch of flap is called for at 95 mph, full flap only when the plane is below 90 mph.

Flaps: set at 20°.

Full flaps: set at 40°

Because of their added drag, many pilots keep the flaps off on a takeoff until the plane has nearly reached its takeoff speed. Without flap, it gains speed more rapidly, and once the speed has been reached, they will pull on half-flap and the airplane fairly scoots into the air. This is by now accepted procedure for taking off from a small field, where there are no long runways for the ship to comfortably build up speed.

THE COCKPIT AND THE INSTRUMENTS

Most drivers tend to hop in their car, start up and take off, seldom bothering to check their dashboard instruments. Some pilots—happily they are few in number—also do. And of these few, most, miraculously, seem to get away with it. But those who don't nearly always make short one-way journeys which, if they are lucky, terminate on a highway or an open field that happened to be conveniently within range when the engine conked out suffering from an acute case of fuel starvation. The cause of the engine failure, in an amazingly high percentage of the cases, is that the pilot just plain forgot to check his fuel gauges and had forgotten to fill them up the night before after he landed.

Familiarity should breed respect—with the airplane and everything about it—

and the pilot who lets familiarity breed contempt seldom has anyone's respect or much of anything else left (including himself) after very long. The airplanes built these days are carefully designed, well-tested pieces of hardware; their engines are reliable and their cockpit dashboards are instrumented well enough to tell a pilot after a very brief check whether everything is working the way it should be.

A safe flight begins where it rightly should—on the ground. It gets under way even before getting in the plane, with a careful preflight check of the outside of the airplane and its control surfaces. Getting in the cabin, the pilot takes the time to look for debris of preceding trips, for example, pencils lying on the cabin floor which can jam in control cables at the worst, or inconveniently jam in the sliding tracks for the seats and be a nuisance.

With the cabin in safe shape, the pilot climbs into the left-hand seat. Actually, on nearly all new planes you simply step up and walk into the front seat, but the language of the biplane era, when pilots really had to climb up, dies hard. Once in the cabin (few ships these days, except for fighters, have *cockpits*), you put your seatbelt on and drop the key into the ignition (see . . . it *is* just like driving a car). But leave the key in the *off* position (no driver ever does that).

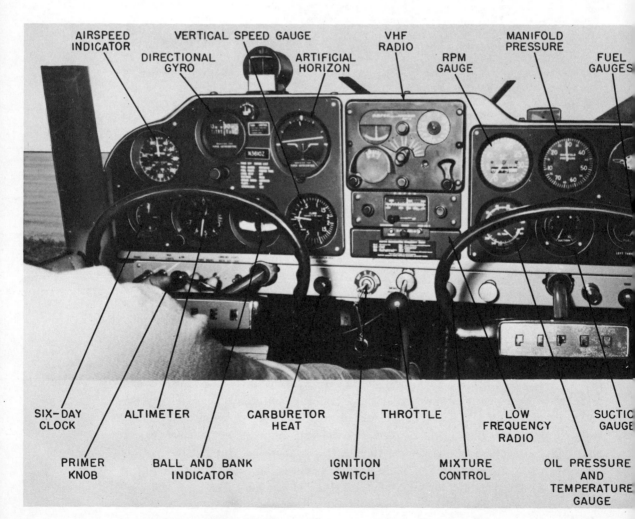

The Tri-Pacer's cabin and instrument panel. The initial bewilderment was gone and familiarity had begun to breed *respect*.

The actual cockpit check is a highly individualistic ritual and almost every instructor has his own favorite rendition. Many prefer the old Air Force system using the slogan:

CIGarets For The Pilot's Rest.

C – Controls.

I – Instruments.

G – Gasoline.

F – Flaps.

T – Trim.

P – Pitch (if the aircraft has a controllable pitch propeller).

R – Run-up.

However, most new airplanes come with a preflight check list in the owner's manual and the actual takeoff check list stenciled on the dashboard. You'll end up with your own system anyway, but as good a method to start with as any is to break down the cabin into two segments—all the control surfaces and the instruments on or near the dashboard.

Every plane has a simple panel dashboard, with a way of checking out the instruments that best fits that type of plane. For years, the Federal Aviation Agency has been trying to get manufacturers to standardize each type of instrument and—most important—their position, so that switching from a Comanche, for example, to a Cessna 210, your eyes would automatically know where to look instead of having to waste valuable time relocating key instruments. But there has been no agreement as yet; indications are that it'll be years before manufacturers do work out a standardized panel. The Federal Aviation Agency is at this time working toward such a standardized panel with *Project Little Guy.*

Most private planes—the Cherokee, Comanche, Tri-Pacer and the Cessna tri-gear series, the 172, 210, and 182 Skylane—have multiple tiers of instruments running horizontally across the dash—in most cases, a bank of three rows of gauges. As the pilot, you will begin your checkout at the far left.

Here's what you'll find on the bottom row of the dashboard:

Circuit Breaker Box. The breakers should all be in the correct "out" position. As in a home, they protect you from fire if electrical shorts develop.

Navigation Light Switch. Always off, except for dusk or night flying. It throws on bright running lights for nighttime takeoffs and landings.

Rotating Beacon. The flashing red light, which can be seen miles away, is now left on even in sunlight by good pilots. Its high-intensity beam can be spotted miles away, even in daylight, especially by planes coming out of the sun toward you.

Parking Brake Knob or Lock. Set "on" before engine start. Like the parking brake on an auto it can be overridden with force, so remember to take it off before rolling.

Electric Fuel Pump. Off, except for takeoff and landing. It guarantees sufficient engine fuel, even in steep turns.

Carburetor Heat. Pushed "in", or off, at start-up, but on damp or cold, icy days, you may want it out as you taxi. It should always be off for takeoff in light planes unless you're in real icing conditions. It prevents the carburetor from icing up in cold, wet weather.

Ignition Switch. Marked "Off . . . Left . . . Right . . . Both," this should be off when not running, and on "Both" for starting and in the air. All plane engines have dual ignitions to be sure the engine is getting electrical juice in case one system ever conked out.

Master Switch. "Off" before start-up. This is the first switch you will put on before starting and when checking your fuel gauges before start-up. The "master" cuts off all electricity flow.

Throttle. Locked "out"—pulled all the way out before start-up. Cracked a quarter of an inch or so just before firing-up to help prime the engine. It takes the place of a car's accelerator but can, of course, be stop-cocked at any power setting.

Primer. This bayonet switch is locked off after the start. You'll want to prime—pull it three or four times—depending on your operations manual before firing up in cold weather. In warm weather it'll need only one or two shots to prime, sometimes none. It shoots fuel into the engine to aid starting.

Mixture Control. Pushed in for full rich on the ground at all times, and kept full rich, generally, until cruising over 3500 feet. It governs the richness of the fuel mixture; at higher altitudes the fuel-air mixture need not be as rich, thus saving on gas consumption.

The actual flight instruments generally begin on the second or middle tier of gauges.

Six-Day Clock. Wound and set, if it is not electric, for recording takeoff time, etc., and for timed turns in the air.

Altimeter. This sensitive barometrically driven instrument, one of the first and still one of the most important of all gauges, is checked right off: its indications change every few hours as the pressure in the air changes. It should always be set to the field altitude. Even if the tower tells you the reading is, for example, 30 point 07, it should still—when set—give the correct *field altitude* on its footage indicator. If it has swung high or low, or if the tower pressure reading does not agree with the field elevation, set your altimeter for the elevation of the airport.

Ball-and-Bank Indicator. This is always approximately centered if it is working correctly, and will tell you the plane's attitude in flight.

Vertical Speed-Gauge. This climb-and-descent indicator, marked in hundreds and thousands of feet per minute, should also be centered at zero or neutral on the ground. It is used to establish and then govern your rate of climb or descent.

Oil Pressure and Temperature Gauges. With the engine off, they shouldn't register anything. They function just as in a car.

Suction Gauge. Scooping in the air for air-pressure-driven instruments, it should also show no reading when standing still.

Fuel Gauges. With master switch off, they read empty—if electric, as most are these days. With the master on, they should correctly indicate the fuel supply. The skilled pilot visually checks his fuel tanks, as well as the gauge, before taking off, in case of malfunction.

Now, in most light planes, you're up to the top or final row of instruments.

Airspeed Indicator. It'll read zero with the plane standing still and, in fact, will not begin to indicate in most cases until the plane has reached a speed of 40 to 45 mph on the ground. It'll have green, yellow and red areas, indicating cruising, maximum maneuvering and never-exceed speeds.

Directional Gyro (or DG). It should be turned to the runway you'll be using for takeoff and then caged or locked by pushing the knob in (and don't forget to uncage it when lined up for takeoff, just before rolling). It tells you the compass heading of the plane, free from the variations or jumpiness in a turn of the magnetic compass.

Aritficial Horizon. Also gyro-driven, it'll look somewhat cockeyed until the engine is started and the gyros have turned over a bit to get themselves lined up. A miniature airplane and horizon on it tell you the attitude of your plane to the horizon at all times.

VHF, and/or Low Frequency Radio. In many planes, they're mounted in the center of the panel; but in quite a few others, they appear at the left or right side. Radio switches should always be off until the engine is started, to prevent battery drain and current surging when starting up. All private-plane communications sets are VHF; some have low frequency sets for navigation and weather broadcast receiving.

Rpm Gauge. This gauge tells you the engine speed in revolutions per minute. Most likely it'll read zero before starting.

Manifold Pressure. Registering actual pressure in the engine manifold in inches of mercury, it generally reads about 30 with the power plant off. Using a column of mercury, it indicates the relative pressure developed in the engine's critical manifold stage. It is so important, and so accurately reflects healthy engine performance, that many pilots "fly by the manifold." They'll set their cruising speed with, say, 27 inches of manifold or "man pressure," rather than by rpm. The manifold is almost like a blood pressure reading hooked into the life system of your engine. When it falters, you can be sure something is not right. If the carburetor is icing up, for example, the first warning (other than an often almost unnoticeable slight roughness in the engine) will come as the manifold pressure begins to drop.

Ammeter. It'll read nothing at all with switches off. But it should indicate a healthy plus output after start-up. You can test it by switching on a radio or lights and look for a slight drop.

The time taken for a complete instrument check is only about 20 seconds, *after* you've gotten used to them. Most of them have no reading, yet your eye, roving the panel *in a pattern,* will quickly note those that do and set up a visual pattern—the same pattern you'll later use in the air.

THE PREFLIGHT

The first part of your preflight is, of course, done outside the plane, checking the aircraft itself. The key item is draining a sample of gas in a small bottle—olive jars are excellent—and checking it to be sure no water is in the gas. Being heavier than gas, water will sink to the bottom. After this, you go on to do a thorough exterior check of your plane. Once again the important thing is to establish a *pattern*. Start at the same point on the plane each time and do a complete circle from left to right. If you choose, start with the propeller. Initially check the prop, making sure it isn't badly nicked or cracked and seeing that the spinner is securely on. Then you'll check your oil level on the engine's left-hand side (in some ships, it's on the right). And while checking the oil, make sure there are no loose wires or leaks of oil or hydraulic fluid in the engine compartment, that engine mounts are not weakened or bent from a hard landing. Secure the cowling carefully. You then move backward a bit, checking the nose wheel and main gear, making sure that the tires are properly inflated and that no brake or hydraulic fluid has leaked down.

Next comes the wing. Check that the ailerons move freely in the right direction, and that the strut is secure, that all surface bolts are secure. Then check the Pitot tube, making sure it's clear to admit the air for the airspeed indicator. After this, check the elevators, rudder and tail section, making sure that all surface bolts are secure and wires firm and that all movable parts have free action. Swing around to the other side of the plane; here you'll check the baggage compartment, repeat the check of the wing, engine, etc.

Now climb into the plane and get ready to start-up. First check the fuel gauges to see if the tanks are full. The rest of the preflight check you do after firing-up. You reach for the master switch.

Flick the master to "on" after making sure no one is near the propeller; even with the ignition off, engines sometimes will turn over if they have a short circuit. The fuel gauges now begin to show readings; pick the fullest gauge and switch your fuel lever to that tank. You look all around the plane—be sure no one is nearby—and then shout "clear" as a warning to anyone approaching that you're about to fire-up. Then switch the ignition to its far right or "both" setting so that the engine's dual magneto electric system is activated, "crack" the throttle a hair and hit the starter button.

The prop windmills unsteadily; the engine whines and coughs perhaps for a split second, then roars into life. The airplane, with its parking brake still locked, vibrates but does not move. You set the rpm gauge at an appropriate speed for a quick warm-up and then glance at the oil pressure gauge. It should already be up near the green, normal midrange; if it doesn't get up to that spot within 30 seconds, something is wrong somewhere in the engine—turn it off or you'll quickly burn out the engine.

But the pressure comes up nicely; the oil temperature begins to register; you flick on the radio and set it for the frequency of the field's ground control frequency or tower (if the field has a tower). Now, after checking for other aircraft and people around your plane, release the parking brake and head for the taxiway. Before entering the taxiway you get permission from the tower; or, if your field has no tower, again check for planes around you or planes coming off the taxiway after landing.

Checking the prop spinner gives Joanne a look at the engine air intakes for debris (birds love to nest in the hood) and allows her to check the propeller for dents and cracks.

Draining gas from beneath the engine before takeoff. And don't just spill it out on the ground; use a glass to see if any water has gotten into the gas.

Draining the wing gascolators on the Tri-Pacer
to test for water in the fuel.

Checking the engine oil level. Just like the family buggy.

But unlike the buggy, the oil rod in a plane engine screws firmly into its socket so that it's
locked there and no oil can spill out or be forced out while maneuvering.

Buttoning-up
the engine cowling.

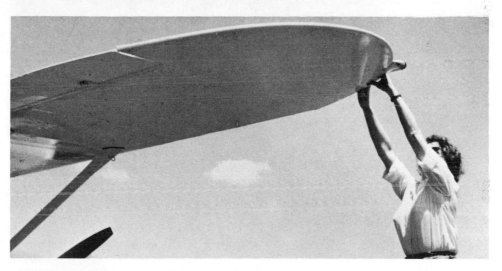

Checking the outer edges of the wing.

Checking the cables and movement of the ailerons.

Now the flaps get checked to be sure they're securely in place; movement is tested from cockpit.

Testing the main wing struts. They should be firmly in place, though at times squeaky. If they come off in your hand, don't put them in the baggage compartment – there's something drastically wrong.

The elevator should be free and move easily.

The support struts that hold the elevator to the wing should be tight and rust- or corrosion-free.

While the rudder won't move very much when the plane is on the ground, it should be checked to see that it is clear of obstructions and undamaged.

The static vents under the fuselage, which are part of the Pitot tube system for measuring airspeed, should be clear of dirt.

The Pitot tube, from which the airspeed indicator gets its input, should be clean and free of all dirt. A bug or dirt in it can throw the airspeed indicator completely off.

Checking the other side of the engine cowling. Everything should be tight and clean with no loose hoses, wires or tubing. A good look underneath will show if any loose oil is lying about, indicating leakage. At this point it pays to look *under* the plane, where leaking oil may have marked the grass or dirt.

COCKPIT CHECK

Key in the ignition. All the way right, to the "both" position.

41

Winged World:
Why the
Airplane Flies

Carburetor heat push-pull knob. All the way in, for "off," on takeoff and dry weather landings. All the way out, for "on," at the first sign of moisture and freezing conditions in the air.

Mixture control knob. All the way in, for "full rich," on takeoff, low altitude flights and landings. Pulled back ever so gently above 4000 feet to conserve gas. But we watched the rpm gauge pulling it back; as soon as it falters in the slightest, you push back in until it regains smoothness and then leave it there; now the engine is correctly leaned-out for maximum cruising economy.

Throttle control. To be used properly, according to the plane's operating manual. In the Tri-Pacer, 2500 rpm for takeoff; 2450 for fast climb; 2350 for cruising; 1800 – 2000 for slow flight in the pattern or for slow-down while flying in rough air.

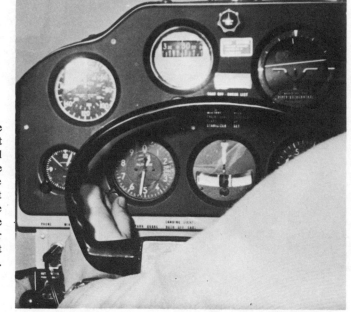

Altimeter. Set it for the correct pressure reading before taking off. The correct setting is *always* the altitude of the field the plane is on, even if the pressure reading differs. In the air, you'll get the current area reading from the nearest tower or range station. And before landing, if at a field with a tower, get the current barometer reading. The altimeter is one of the critically important flight instruments.

The directional gyro. Set it before takeoff, as you line up with the runway – 31 for 310° in this case. More stable than the magnetic compass and not as likely to joggle around in rough air, the DG makes steering in flight far easier. It should be reset every 15 minutes in flight – taking your reading off the magnetic compass while the plane is smoothly holding its heading.

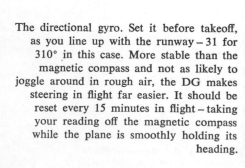

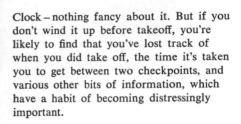

Clock – nothing fancy about it. But if you don't wind it up before takeoff, you're likely to find that you've lost track of when you did take off, the time it's taken you to get between two checkpoints, and various other bits of information, which have a habit of becoming distressingly important.

Trim knob. It turns for nose-up or nose-down trim just like the crank on a car window. Piper sticks to the trim crank; Cessna, and some other firms, use a trim wheel located between both front seats.

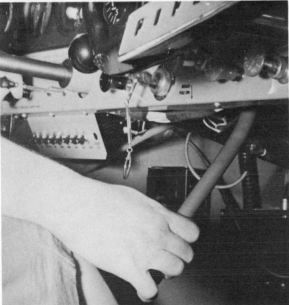

Parking brake. Simply pull back on it – to stop the plane on the ground – *after* rolling-out most of your speed. Too-sudden applications are likely to result in burning out the brakes, damaging the nose wheel and various other unpleasant results. Most private planes use dual toe brakes – located on top of the rudder pedals. The advantage of the single parking brake lever is that it applies pressure evenly to both wheels, thus preventing the plane from veering in either direction because of uneven brake pressure on a single wheel.

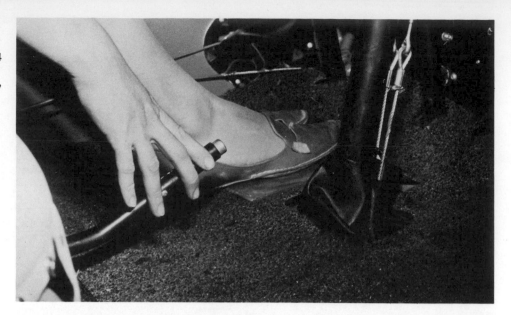

Flap lever: Flaps used on takeoff *after* gaining a good speed shorten the takeoff run about 20 per cent. We found that the Tri-Pacer always seemed to take off better with only half-flap. Full flaps are most useful in dropping the plane quickly, yet under good controlled speeds, into small fields.

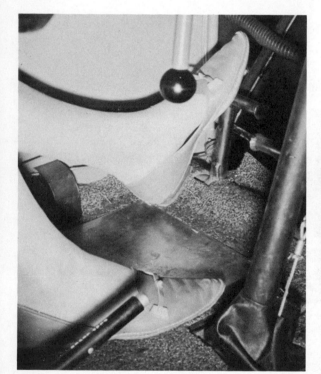

The rudder pedals. Test for freedom of movement.

The radio.
Turn the tuning knob to the field's frequency.

THE RUN-UP

Your last step on gaining the taxiway is to run-up your engine for its pre-takeoff check. Face into the wind. Brakes locked. Check that no plane is so close behind you that your prop blast might upset it. Then smoothly inch the throttle in to your plane's prescribed run-up rpm—in most ships, 1800 rpm. With power up, you switch from "both" magnetoes on to "left" only, then back to "both," then to "right," then back to "both," watching carefully to see that the rpm gauge doesn't drop more than 100 rpm on either mag or the limits prescribed in the operating manual. With the mags checked, you keep power up and inch your carburetor heat knob out to be sure there is no moisture or ice in the carburetor; it shouldn't drop the rpm's more than 50. A small drop in the rpm's is significant in showing that the instrument is in good running order.

CONTROLS

Power check completed, and everything working fine. Now for the controls.

Elevators working freely with full forward and back pressure on the wheel or stick.

Ailerons turning nicely with full play—and they are both moving in *opposite* directions as they should. Careless mechanics, after reworking a plane, have been known to rig both ailerons to work in the same direction, or even worse, in reverse of the way they should be. The pilots who discovered this problem in the air were seldom able to come back to complain.

Rudder working freely in both directions. With the Tri-Pacer and other planes that have interconnected rudder, aileron and nose wheel, the rudder will not turn fully while the plane is standing still.

Flaps. Test them on partial, full and no-flap settings, then set them at the correct takeoff position.

Trim. Adjust for the proper takeoff position. The trim tab enables you to keep the plane in level flight with hands off the control wheel. When your passenger load and baggage varies, the trim tab compensates for positioning of the load and relieves you of the tedious job of constantly holding a lot of pressure on the wheel.

Controls check. Now, you are almost ready to go.

Your eyes roam down the "takeoff check list" on your dash for a quick "Have I forgotten anything at all?" look.

Fuel valves—proper tank.

Fuel valves—proper tank.

Carb heat—checked and off.

Mixture—rich.

Engine gauges—checked.

Flaps up—(unless you need them for a short field).

Trim tab—set for proper load position.

THE TAKEOFF

"Tri-Pacer Triple Two Delta ready to go," you tell the tower or yourself mentally. And you know you are ready—and impatient, since the cockpit check for the first several times around seems to take an unconscionably long time. Make one more important visual check to be sure that there are no planes coming in on final for a landing. All clear.

The runway is yours. The sky beckons. And you know your plane, and you *are* ready. Throttle in . . . almost to the fire wall . . . the engine roaring with takeoff power . . . rolling now . . . the wings quiver momentarily as the airflow grabs on them and you are airborne.

Chapter Three. A BEGINNING

Make no mistake about it—learning to fly *is* harder than learning how to drive a car. Right after World War II, when everybody was talking about a plane "in every back yard," a zealous public-relations-type person coined the phrase that learning to fly was "as easy as learning to drive a car." The slogan is bitterly remembered by the aircraft firms that waited futilely for the boom and saw the unhappy look in the eyes of the disillusioned who had believed the slogan—until they started to learn.

Now the flying boom *is* with us—to stay, most people think—and everyone realizes that while autos operate in just one dimension, airplanes fly in all three and must come back to earth at specified places—airports—not just any handy driveway or side of the road.

When you step into the plane you're going to learn to fly in for your first lesson you will not be able to honestly conceive just how hard or how easy learning to fly will be. But it's a beginning, your beginning in the air, a point to focus on, from which your mind will work forward as you pick up the coordinated skills that are flying. Hundreds of hours, years later, you'll remember that first lesson—what the weather was like, perhaps even what day it was. A new horizon is before you, and nothing about it seems very difficult. It seldom does in the first lesson.

Your instructor mostly familiarizes you with how the airplane flies, extending the first principles he's explained on the ground into actual practice in the air.

Your logbook will be brand-new to flying and so will you as the first real entry goes into your logbook. It is like a first date and the opening of a new romance—your romance with flying. Years later, you'll recall the serial number of the first plane you flew in.

Your logbook looks like this before it fills up with the hundreds of entries—each a flight—that mark your flying career.

That first lesson will only be 45 minutes of flying time in most cases; yet, it'll seem like so much more, like a long cross-country flight. You'll remember the early minutes, when there hardly seems to be very much to do; later on, fully *aware* of everything you are doing, time literally and figuratively flies by, lost in the scores of control and instrument adjustments and other cockpit activity.

But the first honest entry in a logbook should bring things into clear focus. You, as the student, follow the instructor through on the control wheel and the throttle as he smoothly and expertly lifts the plane off the runway. And you're now able to look down from that new perspective at familiar landmarks.

Alone in a clear, calm sky – a beginning.

It takes *skill,* acquired through constant practice in three dimensions, to turn a plane smoothly, with precision, as it *should* be turned, to climb and glide, to handle emergencies like engine failure and to put it on the runway where it *should* be. Flying takes some special training to know how to interpret weather reports and use navigational aids, since an airplane can get lost or get in weather trouble much more easily than the worst of Sunday drivers would ever imagine. The aviation industry has long since burned in effigy at the stake the poor fool who coined the phrase "as easy as driving a car."

Nevertheless, that false image still rests in the minds of some beginners. In case it's one you've been sold on, forget it. It's not that flying is so much more difficult than driving a car (though it *is* more demanding), it's just that the two are different experiences. Vastly different skills are required, and the less time you waste thinking that it's like driving, the faster you'll progress in really learning.

Some of us have sat up in the cockpits of airline jets and watched spellbound as the pilot, a man with thousands of hours of flying time, smoothly, with masterful coordination, worked the controls and throttle in an expert piece of piloting. He did it so fast and so effortlessly that you can easily get the naïve idea that it really *is* easy. It is, for *him*. This happens to all of us. And handling the stick for a few moments yourself doesn't disprove the theory, since the professional pilot will be following you through, correcting your errors, mostly without your being aware of what he was doing. The smile, and easy words they'll give you afterwards, can be misleading.

DATE	AIRCRAFT FLOWN				BREAKDOWN OF			
	Make & Model	Identification Mark	From	To	DUAL		SOLO	
					Received	Given	Day	Night
3/1/58	PA-22	N7222D	SPRING VALLEY	LOCAL	1 :00	:	:	:
					:	:	:	:
					:	:	:	:
					:	:	:	:
					:	:	:	:
					:	:	:	:
					:	:	:	:
					:	:	:	:
					:	:	:	:
					:	:	:	:
					:	:	:	:
PILOT'S SIGNATURE				PAGE TOTAL ▶	:	:	:	:
Julan Bergman				TIME FORWARD ▶	:	:	:	:
				TOTAL TIME ▶	:	:	:	:

Pilot's logbook.

The other kind of wrong impression can come from friends who've learned to fly, who *are* good pilots and are anxious to get you interested. Well and good, as long as they remain friends and don't attempt to become your instructor. In the first place, though they can coach you, they can't write it up in your logbook unless they also happen to have an instructor's rating from the Federal Aviation Agency. And more important, flight instructing—*good* instructing—is an art unto itself. The really topnotch instructor is comparatively rare. There were thousands after World War II and the Korean War, but most have since gone to work for the airlines, gone back to the military or have gotten higher-paying jobs away from instructing. The really good instructor is just what the word implies—he loves to instruct or teach—and there are few who can take the long hours of flying and student errors and yet retain their love for it.

There are even fewer friends who really love to instruct; they'll give you a sampling, then want to fly their plane themselves, so they'll tend to gloss over fine points.

A good instructor is a rare find. Once you've found one, stick to him and to flying.

You'll be best off picking a small airport near your home, rather than a large commercial field with a tower. The small field is seldom tied up with traffic, and you won't have to wait for landing and takeoff clearance from the tower, meaning that you'll get more flying time—and will learn more—in each hour of instruction.

But where you learn is less important than who you learn from—find a good instructor who works for a good school that has planes they keep in good shape. And it won't be hard to locate the best of the schools in your area.

The first time you climb into the left-hand seat of the plane (assuming it's a side-by-side cabin plane), you'll find you've become a different person. After the instructor has headed the plane down the runway and into the air, he'll follow

FLYING TIME				TOTAL TIME ALL CLASSES	REMARKS:
INSTRUMENT					
Aircraft	Link				
:	:	:	:	*1* :00	Familiarization Flight *Jeff* C9174M
:	:	:	:	:	
:	:	:	:	:	
:	:	:	:	:	
:	:	:	:	:	
:	:	:	:	:	
:	:	:	:	:	
:	:	:	:	:	
:	:	:	:	:	
:	:	:	:	:	
:	:	:	:	:	PAGE TOTAL
:	:	:	:	:	TIME FORWARD
:	:	:	:	:	TOTAL TIME

you through as you climb to cruising altitude—which will likely be 2000 feet. Then you'll get busy setting the plane on cruising power (it'll vary from 2300 to 2800 rpm). Next, you'll trim the airplane for level flight, using the trim tab control—a knob which looks like an auto's window crank on the Tri-Pacer, Cherokee or Comanche—or a trim wheel on Cessnas and most other makes. With it, you'll raise or lower the plane's nose to balance the plane in flight, adjusting it for the number and placement of passengers and the weight of baggage and other load.

Adjusted properly for load and power setting, the trim tab makes level flight, takeoffs and landings very much easier. You could fly without a trim tab, but only by exerting constant forward or backward pressure on the wheel—which gets tiresome. With the trim tab, you actually *trim* the plane, taking out excessive nose or tail heaviness.

With your trim tab set, the plane is perfectly balanced and will be flying itself—maintaining its 2000-foot altitude. You'll be flying straight and level—or so it will look. The wings will be nearly even with the horizon or slightly tilted upward—held there by ailerons in neutral setting—and will remain there as long as the control wheel is held in a neutral, centered position.

Now you'll try small movements on the wheel (few planes have sticks any more) to turn the plane. This will seem just like driving a car, to drag out that horrible comparison for the last time. Left on the wheel and your plane turns left; right and she turns right.

Next you'll discover the floor and the rudder pedals, one for each foot, about where the accelerator and brake are in an auto. The instructor will waggle them one at a time, and the plane's nose jogs in the direction of the rudder motion. The rudder controls the movement of the nose.

You will soon learn to use those rudder pedals a little with the wheel. Every movement in an airplane must be *coordinated*—aileron *and* rudder. The aileron turns the plane, but the rudder controls the direction of its nose. Both are needed for a clean turn. Otherwise, you'll skid or mush around on each turn.

In the Tri-Pacer, almost no rudder is needed. It's one of the few planes where the aileron and rudder controls are interconnected to automatically coordinate each turn. And both controls are linked to the nose wheel, for steering on the ground. Flying this way is much easier, until you get back into nearly any other kind of plane, where aileron and rudder are not linked, and have to learn all over to use the rudder to turn the nose in the air and the plane on the ground. There are advantages to both methods, as you'll see later on.

Now you'll try steepening the turns, flipping the wheel more each way, so that your first hesitant maneuvers—perhaps 10° or 20°—now become 30°, still only moderate turns.

Moderate, yet they may seem alarmingly sharp; the plane is partially on its side, one wing high in the air, the other dipping toward the ground, and there is a horrible sensation of falling for most new students. You may have the same feeling so many have, and you'll lean forward queasily to find out if anything is wrong. Nothing is. It is just the normal reaction for a student to have to these first maneuvers. Yet, the earth seems dizzily to reach up at you. After a moment or so, it won't bother you a bit. You'll just shove a stick of gum in your mouth and chew away frantically.

Triple Two Delta in medium left bank. The photographer's plane is turning, too; notice the relationship of the horizon.

Triple Two Delta in shallow right bank. The wing is only slightly tilted.

Unused to such tilting, most people become alarmed at suddenly being turned on their sides. The sensation of fear of falling out of the plane is at first perhaps stark and frightening, largely because most turns in an airplane are comparatively steep —about 30° to 45°, to do the turn quickly and cleanly. At first you'll try to lean away from the bank, fighting gravity, but then you will quickly discover it is impossible to do so. You'll end up sitting straight as a ramrod, having found that to be the most comfortable, as well as the only, position possible.

People sitting up front after the initial experience are seldom bothered by steep turns. It's the passengers in the back seat who suffer. Sitting up front you're busy flying the plane, concentrating on the controls, while in back with nothing occupying you other than wondering what's going on, you're particularly susceptible to suggestive fears about each maneuver.

Your plane will seem to dive nose down each time you turn it. And for good reason; it *is* nosing down. That's exactly what is happening. In a turn, you change the angle of attack of the wing, and destroy part of the airflow over the wing that creates the lift that makes the airplane fly. To compensate for destroying the lift, you have to increase the angle of attack and try to regain some lift by coming back on the wheel to bring the nose up. In a really steep turn, you also have to increase the power to keep the plane at the same altitude.

Just about the time you get used to these mild turns, most good instructors will reach forward and pull the carburetor heat knob out and yank the throttle back.

"Let's try a glide," he'll declare casually, while the panic button in your brain will begin to buzz. He'll start turning the wheel gently one way, then the other, and the plane will spiral down to earth slowly. It'll be shocking at first; the steady roar of the engine is muted and far off now, with a slight whine of the air over the wings the only sound close by.

Gliding. Nose down just slightly, power reduced, Triple Two gracefully sails down toward earth.

Like the maple pods children play with, which gently descend in a circle to earth, your plane will sail downward. You'll be circling first to the right, then reversing yourself back to the left. You will be terribly aware of the earth coming up to meet you at what seems like an incredible speed.

Later on, you'll recall a sense of peace and quiet during the glide. That is, once you get used to the fact that the throttle works as easily in *both* directions— power *on* as well as off.

Now you shove the throttle back in and the carburetor heat knob in, bring the wheel back firmly and the plane returns to straight-and-level flight.

And it is just that simple. The airplane does what *you* want it to do. When you've learned that, and discovered how to make it do what you want it to do— when *you're flying it,* and *it's not flying you*—then you will be on the way to becoming a pilot.

Now it's time for something else new. The instructor quietly will tell you to head for a bridge or point in the distance while trying to hold your altitude, 2000 feet.

His hands leave the wheel and come off the throttle. You'll find that you instinctively and quickly reach for the wheel with both hands. *"One* hand on the wheel," he'll admonish, "the other on the throttle at all times."

It only takes one hand to control the wheel and you want the other hand on the throttle ready to add or take off power in a hurry if you need it.

Your hand will rather uncomfortably settle around the throttle knob, which looks and feels rather like a doorknob. It feels very strange—*one* hand on the wheel—and well it should; most of us have learned to keep both hands on the car wheel, and it takes a while to unlearn a habit.

The plane will now be flying itself very nicely, only you won't be aware of it. Conditioned by too many Hollywood movies, you may feel you should be doing something and begin to jockey the wheel in exaggerated gestures like a movie version of an airline captain. The plane will promptly waggle its wings as if to inquire, "Just what do you think you are doing?"

You'll probably ignore the instructor's quizzical look the first time—he's just trying to make it look tough—and gently nudge forward on the wheel. The ship's nose will promptly start down, and the climb-and-descent gauge on the panel will begin reading like a submarine depth gauge. Alarmed, you'll haul back on the nose and the ship will strain upward, pulling out of the mild dive. Unconsciously, you'll level her off before she starts to stall.

After doing this a few times more, you will begin to wonder just how easy flying is. The instructor puts his hand up in front of your face. He moves it up and down, like a roller coaster moving fast.

Which is what the plane looks like. You're weaving back and forth and up and down through the sky. Now try a light touch on the controls. Just hold them gently.

Hesitantly, you reach for the wheel again, groping for it, like reaching in the dark for a doorknob. Amazingly, the plane doesn't seem to miss your grizzly grip one bit. She flies on her own, all by herself, happy as can be.

Next the instructor will tell you to get your eyes off the instrument panel. With most planes, when the nose is just a trifle below the horizon and the wings sit smoothly a trifle above the horizon, you're flying straight and level. Eventually,

Straight and level. Wings level with the horizon and nose level, though in the cockpit it will appear tilted slightly downward when in level flight.

it will happen. You will come to realize this automatically; you'll also get to know when she's climbing or descending. This is called "seat of the pants flying." You *feel* it, not read it off instruments. Later, you'll learn how to really use the instruments. You may at this point try to imagine some flying skill in the seat of your pants. But your posterior won't tell you any more than it ever did—only that you're sitting on it and feel like you'd just been kicked in that seat of your pants.

You'll fly on for another few minutes before becoming conscious of the fact that the landmark you're headed for seems to be moving to one side. This will seem very odd indeed, since you had pointed the plane's nose right smack at that bridge, tower or factory. You'll be almost to it, but several miles off course.

The instructor, who always seems aware of your unasked questions, will ask, "Where's the wind from?" And you'll suddenly discover that there's a wind in the sky with you even though you can't feel it.

You will find yourself looking around and trying to imagine where the wind *is* coming from. Try to find a factory chimney with smoke billowing outward. The wind will be pushing that smoke in front of it and you can tell the force of the wind by how sharply the smoke is bent.

An airplane is like a sailboat in that its direction is governed to a certain extent by the wind. What you are discovering is that the wind has been pushing the plane off course. Just as in a boat, you must *crab*—aim the nose toward the wind a little away from target—in order to get to where you want to go.

And another thing: Even if there were no wind, the plane would tend to move its nose a little to the left. This is torque at work; the propeller turns in a clockwise direction and it creates a spiral stream of air which moves back over the fuselage, striking the rudder on the left and causing the plane to run to the left. So you correct for torque with a little right rudder. You feel it out. You touch your foot to the right rudder—gently—with no appreciable result. You apply more pressure and the nose of the ship twists right. Too far, you discover. You slacken off, the nose comes straight and stays there. You've discovered just about the right amount of rudder pressure.

Your first lesson is about over. You've had about enough for the first time up. The instructor tells you to fly back to the airport. If you're the unusual and have been really alert, you might have some idea where you could find the airport.

You look at him and wonder if he isn't trying to be funny. He doesn't look much like the spoofing type. Glancing down at the ground, you try to figure where you are. You may have a *rough* idea, since you've probably passed over a familiar road only a few moments ago. It will now seem to have disappeared. You try to look back in the general direction of what you think is the way to the airport; you see nothing, only a line of horizon and some haze. Somewhere, back there, it has to be, and you have to start back sooner or later. That means turning the wheel.

Experimentally, like a surgeon finding the proper amount of pressure with a scalpel, you'll begin ever so gently nudging the wheel. The plane hesitantly starts to turn to the right. This situation continues for about a minute before you notice you aren't getting anywhere; the plane is turning, but you would be across the country before getting it to face in the right direction at the rate it's going.

The instructor comes to the rescue: "Follow me through," he'll declare. His hands take over the wheel and the plane promptly heels over on her side and stays there, pivoting in the air until she comes around 180°—and is then facing in just the opposite direction from the one in which you have been traveling.

The instructor surrenders the wheel to you and this time you feel slightly more secure. You manage to hold the plane about at the altitude it should be and in the proper direction. You even remember to point the nose a little farther north than seems necessary to compensate for the wind that has been drifting you south.

As you circle the airport at 1500 feet, you look over and discover the instructor peering at the wind sock to see exactly which way the wind is blowing (it can change suddenly), and which runway is in use. The wind is out of the north and you notice other planes touching down on runway 5. Add a zero to the 5 and come up with 50°—not north, but as close to north as it was possible to build the runway.

You glide down shaking off altitude, then bank sharply toward the runway threshold. You still have your hands on the wheel, following the instructor through, but your heart won't be in it any longer. The approaches—over trees and towers—are generally appalling to the beginner. Taken on top of his natural unfamiliarity with the plane's rapid descent, they can make the follow-through gesture exactly like that of a zombie. You do it but have absolutely no idea what you're doing. At least this is true the first time. You feel like you're crash-landing in the Amazon jungle.

The plane touches down smoothly in a three-point landing, and you taxi it to the operations building. The instructor makes the first of many scores of entries in your logbook, and you go over again what you have done in the air, and what *needs* to be done.

Flying seems suddenly like mountain climbing—and this first lesson has put you only a few feet past the jump-off point on the trail. But flying is more: it is a skill, an art, an instinct, and science, all wrapped up together; and it requires a tremendous amount of practice before all these things can be blended into one. In fact, as you'll later find out, the practice—the learning process—never stops.

The Tri-Pacer glides downward on final for runway 5 – slow-flighted to 75 mph, with the flaps gracefully dropping it in.

Over the threshold. Levelled off now to shake off the last bit of excess speed and get the plane down to its correct landing speed. At this point, the plane is essentially straight and level.

Flaring out for a landing. The nose is starting to come up gently to reduce speed still further and "drop" the plane in correctly for its touchdown.

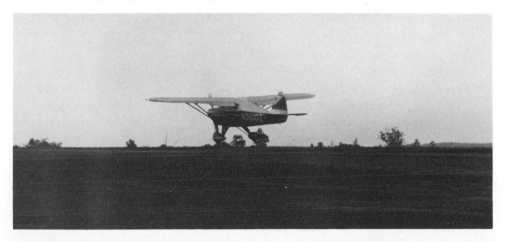

Chapter Four. FUNDAMENTALS OF FLIGHT

The romance that began in your first lesson grows until the third lesson when the honeymoon ends and you begin to face reality. By now, you've learned enough to begin to acquire some respect for the airplane and the air; your initial exuberance begins to taper off into caution and concern.

And you'll discover this in strange ways. It's just about at this time—in your third lesson—for example, that you'll find yourself in your plane, after everything has checked out just fine—you've started the engine, the gauges read normal, you've taxied the plane into position for takeoff—and then you'll discover yourself just sitting there, looking for something, anything that might be wrong, or could go wrong.

It's the familiar beginner's fear finally catching up with you. Like the swimmer cautiously putting his toe into the water before diving in, you hesitantly look things over before moving. There's just one trouble with this. Hesitation at the end of the runway holds up other planes ready to take off. Worse yet, it prevents those lined up on their final approach from landing for fear of an accident. The answer is simple: never take the runway until you're ready to go, and when you do get on the runway, line the plane up quickly and go.

His hands patiently crossed in his lap, as if completely bored with the proceedings, your instructor waits for you to discover your problem. The plane rocks back and forth slightly in the gusty crosswind. It would make you much happier if he had *his* hands on the wheel, at least ready to take over. Looking at him across the front seat, you wonder just how quickly he *could* grab the controls, if you started to veer off the runway. But his face beautifully masks his intent. He is seemingly gazing at the distant hills. Your face mirrors your uncertainty and fear of the crosswind.

"Any old time," he declares quietly.

All right, you think bravely, so I'll drown. Viciously you press the throttle to the fire wall. The trusty engine shudders as it goes to work all at once and too suddenly, then smooths out. The plane just about leaps ahead, then starts to turn off to the right—not suddenly but persistently. The crosswind, but you've forgotten. Left wheel. That helps a bit, but not enough. She is still going toward the trees.

Looking across for assistance shows the instructor still intently watching the run-

Triple Two Delta circles Edgartown, on Martha's Vineyard.

way, apparently braced for the crash if you don't act in time. Actually, his feet have started to sneak onto the rudder pedals. But his casual look and indifference are fully thought out in advance in order to produce action in the fledgling pilot, to make him *think,* to begin developing his judgment and ability to act.

Just at that instant, it all comes together for you as the thought *rudder* stabs through your mind. You quickly hit left rudder and the plane promptly swerves back toward the center line—and keeps right on going to the left. Less left rudder, a bit of right, and she finds the white stripe again and for some unaccountable reason stays there.

A glance across shows the instructor looking at his watch apparently searching to discover just how much more pain he'll have to suffer before *this* lesson is finished. You gather speed now, galloping away, swallowing up what remains of the runway. The airspeed indicator moves up: 45, 50, 55, 60, 65. He looks around to see what all the delay is. *He* didn't need any airspeed indicator to know the plane had sufficient speed to get off.

65, 70, 75 . . . just as the blacktop vanishes under the wheels, you yank back on the stick and the ship jumps away like a fighter plane and climbs out at a fantastic angle. His face bears a look of distinct anguish.

"That was just fine," he says hollowly. "Except now you know you should have taken off long before—at about 65 miles per hour. You would have cleared the trees more safely and saved the tires and landing gear from that jolting around on the runway. Don't hold the wheel forward, ease it back a bit."

The airspeed now registers 90 mph. The altimeter, 850 feet. "Now," he says disgustedly, almost echoing your own mind, "let's start *flying* the airplane the way it should be flown. First off, let's make a proper departure from the runway pattern"—400 feet above the airport height (if your airport's altitude is at sea level), a 90° left turn for the standard pattern before departure. You heel over hard on her left wing, turning the wheel too steeply.

"A *gentle* turn," he admonishes. "*All* turns near the ground are gentle turns. You don't have the room to recover the plane if you go too far and she stalls on you." The wheel returns to neutral. Now keep on climbing . . . 600 feet over the airport . . . a 45° bank to the right, continuing in a shallow turn. This is our exit from the airport's traffic pattern. At an airport with a tower, this is the point where you tell them you're leaving their pattern.

"Take her on over to the practice area," the instructor declares and sits back. "Climb to 2000 feet." You drone along in the climb heading north to the air-traffic-free area designated as the local practice area. A deck of scattered cumulus clouds sits just above you as you arrive at 2000 feet. But they are so thin and so scattered that any plane descending through them would easily spot you in plenty of time.

When you are over the practice sector, he tells you, "Okay, cruise power and trim her for level flight." Pulling back on the throttle, the engine slides back from 2450 to 2350 rpm, the recommended cruise-power setting for most light airplanes. Now a few turns of the trim knob directly overhead. But the plane seems to either want to climb or glide—never to stay in level flight.

The trick is simple. Ignore the nose in front of you and trim the airplane by the angle of attack of the wings, or more truly, since you can't see the top of the wing in a high-winged plane, by the way the bottom of the wing sits on the horizon. In a low-wing ship, however, you judge by the way the top of the wing sits on the horizon. The plane is trimmed correctly when the wing is sitting just about even with the horizon—except for the frustrating ups and downs of the air currents, which can often convince you that it isn't trimmed at all.

Now you begin working through the basic regime of climbs, banks, turns and glides. "Fly straight ahead," you're instructed, "and hold your compass heading." The directional gyro compass (or DG) reads 10°, just east of north. But not for long; that brisk wind on the ground, which almost always is stronger high in the sky, is pouring out of the west. The plane keeps moving to the east or right— 15°, 20°, 22°. Cutting in with left-wheel movements only turns her too far to the west. Rudder again—remember to keep the nose pointed straight. Experimenting with the right pedal soon gets the desired result; the ship creeps back to 10° and stays there.

There is also some experimenting now to show the proper use of, and pressures on, the rudder. Ordinarily, coordinated controls are the rule: left aileron, left rudder. In fact, most of the time after the plane is set up on its proper course, you can leave the aileron alone and make the fine steering adjustments with rudder only.

With the plane set up, you'll begin working on simple turns—90° or more in all directions. Remember, the degree of the turn has nothing to do with the degrees of a bank—a 90° turn, for example, can be made with 15°, 30° or 45° banks.

"All right, make a gentle 90° turn to the left," the instructor calls out. Look right and then left, just like a car at an intersection before turning. The airplane *is* at an intersection in the sky. Raise each wing slightly, to be sure no one is descending in your direction or that you are not cutting into another plane's lane. This is called "clearing yourself." Some instructors and many pilots still like to hear "clear right . . . clear left" before entering into any turn.

A gentle turn, no more than 15° of bank, wing slightly down in the direction you want to go. You slide past 15° quickly, and the artificial horizon shows the plane slipping toward a moderate bank—30°. Opposite aileron and rudder movement bring her back, but you are already halfway through the turn. What is worse, the altimeter now reads 1800 feet; you've lost 200 feet so far in the turn. Pulling back on the wheel, she climbs past 2000 feet again.

It's no trick making the 90° turns. The real trick is doing them without losing or gaining more than 100 feet of altitude as required by the rules and safe flying methods. You waste no time in learning the source of trouble and eliminating it: when the plane is banked into a turn, its lift ceases to be straight up from the ground and becomes angled toward the horizontal. The lift, in effect, *pulls* the aircraft to the side as well as straight upward. To keep at the altitude you were at when you began the turn, the plane has to have enough lift to continue to support its weight. What this means, simply stated, is that in a turn you need *more* lift than that required for straight-and-level flight. In a turn, lift is spilled out of the wings and the plane will tend to drop.

So more lift is needed. It can be gotten in only two ways: with more airspeed by giving the plane more throttle, or by pulling back on the wheel to increase the angle of climb. The surest way is with more throttle or *gentle* back pressure on the wheel. Pulling back on the wheel too suddenly, while it solves the problem easily for moderate banks, can drop the plane into a dangerous stall if the pilot isn't super-careful.

Another point easily overlooked—a point tied in with the turn—is that the plane's stalling speed goes *up* or increases during banks. The Tri-Pacer, for example, with a normal stall speed of 49 mph in straight and level flight (without flaps), will stall at just under 52 mph in a 20° bank; at nearly 54 mph in a 30° bank; at close to *70* mph in a steep, 60° bank; and at roughly 120 mph in an 80° bank, an excessive degree of bank into which the plane should never be put. This should be obvious, since the stall speed is nearly as high as the Tri-Pacer's (or any plane's) maximum cruising speed near the ground.

Knowing all this, turns and banks become far easier. In the 90° turn, you nudge the throttle in just a little more, to about 2375 rpm, and the plane stays glued to 2000 feet. But not the first several times. It takes practice and experimentation. First, without using extra power, simply use more elevator and watch the plane lose altitude. Then, as the elevator pressure continues, watch the plane gain altitude, but lose airspeed. Finally, only by adding power, see the plane maintain both its airspeed and altitude.

The 90° turn is the easiest of all—turning your head in either direction about as far as it goes without snapping is roughly 90°—and you can see that much from most any cockpit. But beyond 90°, the compass becomes an instrument to really pay attention to. Curiously, a 45° turn is also harder; people just don't think in 45° terms, but easily—through the habit of driving, perhaps—in 90° or in U-turn—180°—terms.

Practicing the full-about 180° maneuver requires more time and effort. For one thing, if you want to make the turn in a reasonably small amount of area, it has to be a reasonably steep bank, perhaps 30° or 50°.

A good way to go through the turning torture (which it unfortunately is for many beginners) is to make all three basic turns—90°, 180° and 360°—first in gentle 15° banks. A turn of 360° is, of course, nothing but a full circle, or continuing the 180° turn for another 180°; and the 180° merely means following through on the 90° turn for another 90°. After all three have been worked over in 15° form, you may try 30° or moderate banks for the same three turns. The only difference, other than watching the heading of the plane a bit more carefully, is that the plane will want to lose more altitude. So still more power is required. And in the steeper banks, 45° or more, even more power and more pulling back is needed; more lift has been lost and more than 20 mph has been added to the plane's stalling speed.

After you've gotten gentle and moderate banks down fairly well, you begin to work into climbing turns. This proves to be easy, since most takeoffs—clearing the airport—are a series of climbing turns. But there are several things to remember. Most important—*all* climbing turns are gentle turns. The reason will become apparent the first time you try one: with the airplane banked into a turn while its nose is raised at the same time in the climb maneuver, it is all too easy for the pilot, without realizing it, to haul the nose too far up and find himself with little or no warning in a stall. It can happen even more easily when you remember that the banking maneuver is *increasing* the stall speed *at the same time* that the plane is coming closer to a stall attitude in its climb. There will be no problem though, if you just keep the climbing turns gentle.

From the first soaring attempts at climbing turns, you will, over the span of several lessons, work forward into the entire manual for turns. You practice gentle (15°), medium (30°) and steep (45°) straight-and-level turns; then the same routine through climbing turns, until you feel like you'll never fly straight again, that you are permanently angling through the air on your side. Then down the scale again for gliding turns: right, left, 45°, 90°, 180° and 360°, and graceful spirals.

One of the major difficulties many pilots experience when starting out is the inability to picture their maneuvers fully. They can see what it looks like from the inside of the cockpit and on their instrument panel; they can grasp to a certain extent their attitude from the wing or nose attitude. But it is nearly impossible for them to grasp the full meaning of the maneuver – the way their plane looks from the outside and the way this is demonstrated on their instruments *at the same time*. Here is the way it will appear to you, inside and outside. . . .

Straight and level, with the plane trimmed up before beginning a maneuver.

The same attitude, from the inside. Note that the artificial horizon, the topmost instrument to the left of the radio, is perfectly centered.

Shallow bank to the left. Shallow is defined as about 15°. In this exterior view, the Tri-Pacer is passing through 15° and is beginning a steeper bank.

And from the inside. The three white lines on the artificial horizon signify 30°, 60° and 90°. The Tri-Pacer is midway at 15°. The artificial horizon shows the horizon's relationship to the plane, not the plane's to it. The wings remain fixed on the horizon – *it* changes.

Medium bank to the left. The left wing is dipped into the horizon at a 30° attitude.

And the same maneuver inside. The artificial horizon is just on the 30° line.

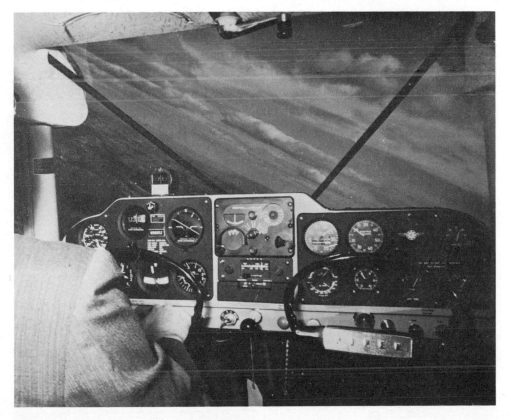

Steep bank to the left. Forty-five degrees or more is considered a steep bank. In this picture the plane is actually somewhat beyond 45°.

From the inside, with the artificial horizon indicating nearly a 75° bank. Banks beyond 45° are not only unnecessary most of the time, but dangerous, especially at low altitude. Note the severe angle to the horizon and the clouds ahead of the windshield.

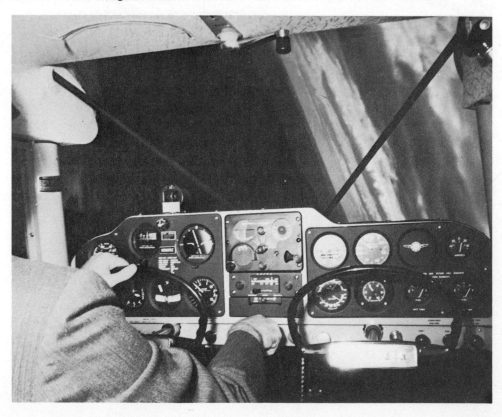

Fundamentals of Flight

Back to straight and level before beginning right turns.

Shallow bank to the right from the inside. About 20° is indicated.

Steepening a medium bank. The artificial horizon is going through 45°.

Climbing – wings level. The plane remains on a plane with the horizon and only its wings angle upward. This is a medium climb, about 400 feet per minute.

And from the inside. The artificial horizon is below the wing level to indicate the climb.

Steep climb, wings level. Throttle in for full power, nose up and climbing out at the plane's maximum safe rate – 800 fpm.

The artificial horizon shows the attitude; the real horizon is lost below the nose. The rate-of-climb gauge, not yet caught up, reads 700 fpm.

Anyone Can Fly

Climbing turn to the left. Left wing down, nose hauled up. The maneuver is only attempted at full power; otherwise the steep bank can result in a loss of altitude and ultimately a stall.

From the pilot's-eye point of view. The artificial horizon indicates a 30° climbing turn. The rate-of-climb gauge reads 450 fpm.

Climbing turn to the right. As you see it, from the cockpit. Just under a 30° indication, climbing at 450 fpm.

Glides – first with wings almost level, nose slightly down. Speed is controlled at 90 mph, rate of descent is about 600 fpm.

Gliding turn to the left. Entered and held as a shallow bank, at about 15°. Speed is held down – here it's about 95 mph and the rate of descent is about 800 fpm.

Steep gliding descent to the left.

Shallow gliding turn to the right. Here it's shown that in a glide the nose does not have to be sharply down.

Steep gliding descent to the right. In flying a tight pattern around an airport, steep gliding banks are often necessary.

Out of this air work, slowly but surely, emerges the coordinated skill that goes into piloting—the beforehand knowledge of just how much aileron and rudder and when to apply it—and the gradual acquiring of seat-of-the-pants "feel," the mysterious built-in instrumentation of the pilot, which teaches the body what attitude it and the airplane are in; also, the gradual recognition of the reassuring sound of your engine performing its work in each different attitude.

And there also comes the first knowledge of the unseen but strongly felt wind— wind to throw you off in a turn, wind to carry you away from a runway after being lined up, wind to make your plane go too fast or too slow at critical moments until you learn to sense it and act to master it, wind to lift you up or pull you down. While wind cannot truly be mastered, it can be used or counteracted—and must be—before the would-be pilot can truly become an airman.

The earth below becomes a point of reference from which to learn to gauge the wind. The lesson of wind is so simple that it generally becomes confused during the learning process, when it is mixed in with scores of other items.

The lesson is clear: when the wind blows *at* you during a turn, it will push the plane back away from the turn, and you will fall short of the turn. When the wind is blowing from behind or with you, it will push the plane too far, carrying you beyond the area in which you want to turn. But the wind behind can be stopped from carrying you too far if you steepen your turn. The wind into you actually helps you turn so that a shallower bank will do the job; with a steep bank you'll turn too soon.

One word of warning: no matter which way the wind blows, never make steep turns when close to the ground. The rough, bumpy air near the ground may result in treacherous conditions if a steep turn is attempted. A sudden gust, for example, can push your upper wing higher while the wind may die under the other wing. The bank will be dangerously steepened without altitude for a safe recovery. This is especially true of downwind turns at low altitude: when the wind behind you pushes the plane at a healthy ground speed, you may be fooled into allowing your airspeed to get too close to stall speed. The only speed that counts at such times is the airspeed—the velocity at which you and your airplane are moving through the air currents.

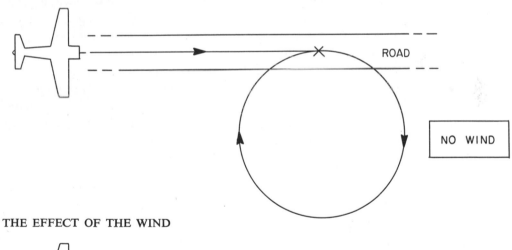

THE EFFECT OF THE WIND

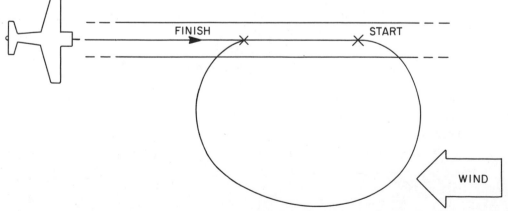

More is learned about wind in gliding turns than in any other maneuver. With the airplane flying slow and, in effect, without power, it will respond to the wind more swiftly. So there is no better way of learning about wind.

Gliding turns come easily, and somehow seem less like work. The glide itself comes first. And before it, comes setting the plane up for the glide: checking below and on all sides, then pulling out carburetor heat (since the engine with power drastically reduced will tend more easily to ice up), finally hauling back on the throttle, pointing the nose slightly down and trimming her to a maneuvering speed of 80 mph. After you run through it a few times, you'll begin making gliding turns to the right and left—practicing, in effect, the first part of the landing.

The gliding maneuver, and the quiet with the power reduced, somehow combine to give the flier a feeling of freedom and grace. Together, they are the reward for work well done—and rest assured, unless you are born with wings rather than arms, the first few lessons *will* seem like hard work.

Depending on your own mental and emotional feelings about flying, the progress of learning can be nerve-racking. Most people are in reality learning two things at the same time: how to fly an airplane and how to conquer the instinctive fear of the air that has been inbred into man—an earth-and-water creature— over thousands of years. Usually, skill and confidence come together; about the time you learn what your hands and feet should be doing with the ailerons and rudder, your palms become somewhat less sweaty and your leg muscles a good deal less frozen.

Some beginning fliers never experience such qualms about their own airworthiness. Most of us, however, do, and it is a good thing, too. This instinctive fear will unconsciously drive you to be cautious at the controls of an airplane. The highways would be much safer if the average driver behind the wheel of a car had as much fear of what he did on a layer of blacktop as he does on a cushion of air.

Each time you finish a lesson you'll find your confidence mounting, and your instructor, with a pretense of casualness, will work on further building up your confidence. Generally, with about ten minutes of the fifty-minute lesson remaining, he'll say, "Okay, take us back to the airport." Then, he'll light a cigaret, or open a flight manual and artfully pretend to ignore you. The first few times, if your instructor tries this maneuver, you may feel cheated. After all, shouldn't he be giving you more air work or tips?

In reality, you've already had as much as you can absorb in a lesson, and pushing it any more would simply work your fatigue to the point where you'd be making silly errors. The other point is that the instructor is in effect removing himself from the plane, letting you fly solo long before you are qualified to, but placing you in the position of *thinking* solo—for yourself—and figuring your own reactions to situations. Actually, he'll be most carefully gauging the attitude of the plane, and sneaking looks at the instruments.

The other interesting thing about a good instructor is that he'll throw you into situations long before *you* think you are ready for them. After the lesson, when the plane has found its way back to the airport, he'll refuse to land it. *"You* do it," he'll declare.

Then he'll make you figure out, step by step, what should be done. First you'll circle the field about twice as long as needed, trying to build up confidence in your

ability to land the plane. Remembering ground school, and his advice, you seek
out the wind sock.

Runway 28; that means 280°, you recall. First, the plane runs *with* the wind
in the traffic pattern—the *downwind leg*—after cornering into the leg at a 45°
angle. That is easy. Turning into the second leg of the landing—the *base leg*—
seems a bit awkward. It is, too, since the wind is now carrying the plane all over
the area without your being fully aware of what is happening. The *final approach,*
the third leg, when the plane is lined up with the runway for landing, is equally
interesting. A straight line *can* have curves, all over the place, when the wind is
gusting back and forth.

Between the skittering, the plane manages to slow itself down to a good approach speed—75 mph. The best part is the landing. It turns out to be beautiful.
The plane touches down on all three wheels, as gentle as a feather landing on
water.

And it feels good, as if you'd really learned something. Pride wells up in you
as the plane rolls out and slows on the runway. Not quite an hour's flying, but it
seems like a week. When you turn off the engine and get out, flying is the greatest
thing in the world to you—and landings, they are a snap.

The instructor hardly has to tell you it was a darn good lesson. You know inside
you've done well and cleared another hurdle, even if you somehow suspect that
the good landing was due more to luck than skill.

Chapter Five. THE AIRPORT

For most people an airport is a place they take a cab to, or park their car at to get aboard a big commercial plane. For the flier, it soon becomes a kind of second home. It is, above all, the place where his flight begins and ends. But airports, small ones especially, soon become far more than just a place to land at, refuel, park your plane and then go home. More often it grows on you to the point where after parking the plane, you head in to the operations office for a Coke or a cup of coffee to talk out problems and exchange stories with fellow fliers.

To begin with, the airport you fly at may be anything from a single grass strip to a bigger operation with two paved runways in different directions, or a major general aviation field, on the order of Teterboro, the Port of New York Authority's business and small plane (4500-foot runways) field on the outskirts of New York. Like as not, it will not have a tower; only the major airports, with a pretty fair number of multi-engine airplanes and considerable traffic, rate a tower, which is a government installation run by the Federal Aviation Agency. However, this does not mean you are without radio. Many small fields boast *Unicom,* the pilot's general advisory and information radio frequency, which is on either 122.8 or 123.0 megacycles. While Unicom is not intended for traffic control in the skies over any airport, a call will get you good advice—the latest poop on the winds, runway conditions, what services are available, even information on calling a cab.

But many small fields, especially those far out in resort or sporting areas, do not have Unicom. The pilot is on his own for landing conditions. This means checking the latest sectional chart, which will tell you where the field is, what kind of runways it has and how long they are, the field's altitude, and whether it has lights. The back of the chart will add types of mechanical service and fuel available, unless the field is so small it is not listed, or is a private facility. But your job is not finished—remember that the chart may be as much as six months old. Next step is to check NOTAMS (Notices to Airmen) and the *Airman's Guide,* which will tell you the current (within a few days) condition of the field. NOTAMS mention, for example, if a runway is out of action, if the field itself is closed, obstacles, frequency changes and any number of other important bits of information.

And another good thing to do before taking off for a strange field is to ask your fellow fliers about it. Things are often not as they seem; the field may have a new hazard that has developed so recently it hasn't turned up in a NOTAM as yet.

After all this, the final thing to do before taking off is to file a flight plan (if the field you're headed for is any real distance—more than 100 miles—away) with the nearest federal aviation tower or range station. They can be filed by phone or, if that doesn't seem practical, after your takeoff by using the radio in your plane.

All this preparation pays off in a safer and quicker landing. Every airport has a landing pattern—either a right- or a left-hand pattern. This means simply that approaching the airport you fly on a definite side of the active runway— either to the right or left—and then turn either right or left on your base leg toward your final approach. Unless otherwise noted, most airports have left-hand patterns; the choice lies with the field operator, the tower, or FAA specifications. Frequently, large commercial fields—those with dual side-by-side runways—will have two *opposite* patterns, to better separate their traffic, or may choose a right-hand pattern to avoid a hazard or housing development. Here you *must* use radio. Most major fields now require two-way radio in all planes.

But most fields have only one pattern. When they have a tower, the controller will tell you which way the pattern is being flown. When they do not have any radio aid, watch the other traffic landing to get the direction of the pattern or, if there is no other traffic, assume it to be a left-hand pattern.

After discovering or settling on the pattern (assuming you have already checked out any unusual hazards, such as high radio or television transmitting towers, buildings, trees near the airport), the big question is, which runway is in use. The wind itself is the first and generally the best clue. If it is pouring out of the northeast, for example, from about 40°, the runway in use will generally be that closest on the compass to 40°—*if* that runway is open and safe.

No work at all is involved if the field has a tower or Unicom; then from about 10 miles away you can call in and get back the answer. A sample answer is: "One Zero Zulu . . . report downwind for runway 4 . . . wind 10 knots from 40 . . . altimeter 30 point 12 steady." And don't forget that altimeter setting; if the field does not have a tower and you can get no altimeter setting, remember that the field may not be at sea level. You have to fly your pattern at the standard pattern altitude—800 feet *plus* the field's height (which is listed on all aerial charts)—or if it is 300 feet above sea level, a pattern of 1100 feet. (But remember some fields have 1000-foot patterns—not 800 feet—or 800 feet for light single-engine ships and 1000 feet for multi-engine aircraft.)

Now, assuming the field has no radio aids, you still have to find which is the right runway. Every field has one or more of three devices to help you—either a tetrahedron, a wind tee or a wind sock.

The tetrahedron, which is just what it seems to be but doesn't look it, is a four-sided, sort of rectangularly hull-shaped object. Its point faces toward the runway in use.

The tower at Teterboro Airport.

The wind sock. Here it's indicating a mild crosswind.

The tetrahedron, with its pointer toward the active runway.

The wind tee, a T-shaped metal or wooden object painted white in most cases, points into the wind, with the long bar of the T facing the direction that the winds are blowing out of.

The wind sock, while it does not always indicate the active runway, is the old reliable and still the most valuable airport aid. It tells you most surely the direction of the wind. After you get used to it, it will also tell you the relative intensity of the wind. A sock standing straight out, for example, is a sure clue that the field is far from becalmed, that the wind is booming along the open strips. When the sock stands slack, you know there isn't any real wind. There are exceptions: the sock often is above or below the threshold of the runway in use, where the wind may be stronger or weaker than the sock seems to indicate. A word of caution: be wary of fields where the sock stands higher than the runways—trees, pits and ledges can cause dangerous turbulence during landings.

Wind tee at Williamsport, Pennsylvania, Airport. It shows that the wind is quartering off the active runway – which runs across the picture. The L markings indicate that the pattern is left-hand. The foot of each L is the direction of the base leg and the upper bar is the course for final approach. At Williamsport, the left-hand approach is to avoid the hazard of mountains to the side of the airport.

With all these items understood, the pilot is free to concentrate on the artful skill needed for his landing—his mind is not chock-full of nagging doubts. If these points seem belabored, just remember that the great majority of all accidents happen either on takeoff or landing. Landing at a strange field, or even at your home base, is not like hopping down to the corner grocery. It is an *event*— and when you stop thinking of it as an event, that's the right time to take up bowling or bridge and give up flying. Not that it's hair-raising or deadly dangerous every time; but good pilots are *wary* ones. There are "old pilots and bold pilots," the flying satire goes, "but no old, bold pilots."

The reason every landing is an event rather than a taken-for-granted routine is that no two landings ever are or even seem to be exactly the same. The wind is never quite the same; neither is your skill, the attitude of the airplane, your approach to the field, and many other factors. This is why the pilot who can land his plane at any field and do it smoothly under gusty conditions or crosswinds, is a man who has not only practiced, but knows his skill, and never forgets about any item on his check list. The concentration required, far from being depressing, is part of the "intense relaxation" that makes flying different and challenging; and paradoxically, a relaxing, but not too relaxing, avocation.

The pilot who ground-loops the airplane, veers off the runway, lands short, or overshoots, is almost invariably the fellow who relaxed himself into a semicoma while landing and forgot that a big part of the fun is the work itself, and the satisfaction that results from doing the work well.

And the work is not over when you've touched down and are rolling out. Somebody else is behind you, or to one side, waiting to take the runway, so you want to get off the active runway at the first taxiway, or where the tower may tell you. If the field has a tower, you'll want to switch to ground control frequency as soon as you leave the active runway and get approval or instructions for taxiing to the place where you'll hangar or tie down. Taxiing in or rolling out from his landing, many a sorry pilot has carelessly forgotten about a ground hazard—an unrepaired hole, a new landing light, or even other planes charging out for a takeoff.

And even before you get ready to relax, if you're landing in a pouring crosswind, there's rolling out. It's just at that moment that the wind will unexpectedly gust a little bit extra and your neat little airplane will be dropped on one wing. Incidents such as these are so damaging to one's morale—and wallet—that they are best avoided altogether.

The time to relax is *after* you've tied the ship down or handed it over to the line boy. You'll have done your job well, and begun to grasp the joy, fun, or whatever special satisfaction you get from the concentrated skill of flying.

And if your landing was rough or a bit bumpy and you feel guilty, depressed and embarrassed about it all at once—as you will for the first hundred landings— don't worry about what the other characters around the airport are thinking. If they're brand-new students, they'll probably be thinking that it was just like the last bumps-and-grinds routine they put the ship through. In the unlikely event that a wiseacre makes some derisive crack, just tell him you were trying to learn by watching from *his* errors, but haven't quite gotten the hang of it yet. . . .

THE AIRPORT

A variety of private and business planes on the apron at Teterboro Airport.

Anyone Can Fly

Looking out from the tower at Teterboro.

This is the kind of service pilots never get. If you're lucky, one attendant will come out promptly to fuel your plane and check your oil. This scene is pure fantasy.

Chapter Six. TAKEOFFS AND LANDINGS

An airplane rolling on the ground is like a fish struggling to get back in water: it is out of its medium. It has wheels and brakes to help it while earthbound, but it is still a winged creature; and until it has built up its momentum to takeoff speed, it is prone to behave somewhat awkwardly. It is precisely during these strange seconds, while the plane is losing its earthly characteristics and picking up the lift that makes it fly, that many pilots get into trouble.

"I don't know what happened. . . . I just lost it," goes the classic excuse dumbfounded students (and some pilots who should know better) give after ground-looping the plane or, for inexplicable reasons, running off the runway into the landing lights. What is even more frustrating is that most of them honestly *don't* know what happened.

Things were going along fine until the gusty crosswind picked up a trifle, or the plane hit a deep puddle, or. . . . Since an astoundingly high percentage of minor and major accidents and incidents take place during the takeoff and landing, the idea is never to "lose it"—never, even in the case of mechanical failure, to let things get out of hand. The way to do this is so painfully simple that many pilots just plain ignore it: practice until every takeoff and landing is like a chess game—a series of carefully planned moves *anticipating* (there's that ubiquitous word again) any move that the enemy might make (the enemy being sudden wind gusts, mechanical failure or the erratic actions of another pilot).

Now the work and concentrated fun of patterns begins: flying a rectangular box around and around the field as you build up your skill in landing. Your preflight is completed. You've warmed the plane up, and safely (that means slowly) taxied to the edge of the active runway after getting tower clearance or double-checking on traffic if you're at a towerless field.

Turning the nose of the plane into the wind to keep the engine cooler and the plane away from the rocking of the wind, you now do your run-up—checking magnetoes, carb heat, controls, flaps and the *complete* takeoff check list printed on the dashboard (if the plane doesn't have one, type it out and tape it on the dash). There's nothing like skimping on the check list for putting nagging—and possibly dangerous—doubts in your mind after you've begun your takeoff roll and something goes wrong. The run-up, done while faced away from other planes, ought to be complete.

Just before entering the active runway, swing the ship for a final look to see if

Setting her down.

any traffic is on final approach or far enough along on base leg so that you should wait.

The plane landing always has priority on the runway; you can't know whether he's short of fuel or needs to make it in this time without going around. Remember that his speed has been cut and he's lost altitude and that extra margin necessary in order to make quick and safe recoveries. Any time you're tempted to make a run for it, to get off in a hurry, even though another ship is halfway in on its final, just stop for a second, long enough to remember that *you* could be the pilot in that plane—low on fuel, nearly in trouble, or tired and maybe unable to make it around the pattern again. Also remember that FAA rules flatly declare that the plane about to land always has priority for the runway.

Now you're ready to start rolling for takeoff. You point the plane straight down the runway and just before pushing the throttle in, shoot a last look at the wind sock, for a final check at what the wind is doing. It's probably just where it was when you taxied by on the way for run-up, but that final look erases any lingering doubt from your mind and more sharply acclimates your senses to what to expect.

If the wind is scurrying across the runway, and it's a crosswind takeoff, you are

now prepared for it. Your hands and feet, on ailerons and rudder, are waiting to
sense the amount of pressure needed on the controls to hold the ship glued to the
center line as you pick up speed.

Smoothly, you move the throttle in, not to the firewall (unless on a short field)
but just short of it, reaching the right amount of power for takeoff and yet not
working the engine into a premature session in the shop after being chronically
overworked. The plane leaps forward eagerly with its newly found power and begins gathering momentum. Now, even if it's a flat calm with no wind, she may
begin to veer ever so slightly to the left from torque effect (the pulling motion of
the propeller which tends to move the nose of the ship in the direction that the
prop rotates) and you answer with right rudder. If it's a ship with nose-wheel
steering, it may not require much, if any, rudder to hold her straight.

With a Tri-Pacer, rudder and nose wheel are linked, so you're steering full-
time. You shoot a look over at the airspeed indicator, which still reads 0. It'll
stay that way, too, until about 40 mph when it suddenly begins to register. But
forget about the airspeed indicator, except for one or two split-second glances.
You'll get to know instinctively when the plane is ready to lift off.

In most tricycle planes you'll know pretty easily. The nose wheel begins to
bump rather heavily as you gather speed. The first thing to do is to come back on
the wheel a little bit, just enough to rotate the wheel off the ground in order to
save it from getting banged around unnecessarily.

Your speed is now over 55 mph. The plane begins to feel "loose" and lighter
in the wings. The wheels seem to have lost some weight on the runway; all of a
sudden it becomes unavoidably clear, regardless of the airspeed indicator, that
the ship wants to fly and is ready to do so.

But, playing safe, you hold it just a few seconds longer, until the speed is
hovering around 60 mph, giving you that extra margin of safety. (When the plane
is lightly loaded, or when you are attempting a short field takeoff, there'll be
times when you'll have to get it off the ground a few seconds sooner, but in
general, the faster the better—within reason.) Now, your airspeed is safely over
stalling-speed worries, and you have that extra margin of safety. It's time to fly.

Deftly and smoothly, you pull back on the wheel, giving the plane time to
respond, not trying to push it into jumping off ("jacking it off the ground" is what
pilots call it). The plane unhesitantly points her nose skyward and smoothly lifts
off into the sky.

Next comes the shocker for the average student: once you get it off the
ground about 8 feet, you bring the nose *back down* ever so slightly to pile up a
little bit more speed for a safer, swifter and smoother climb-out. If you'd been
monitoring your airspeed indicator and you'd started the takeoff at 62 mph, you'd
find that the speed barely remained that high when you lifted off.

Remember, the plane is still in the act of *building up* speed when you take off,
and when you increase the angle of attack for the takeoff, you temporarily lose
some of your speed. So its wings level now for a few seconds until the speed gets
up to about 75 mph, then you climb out cleanly, not zoom straight up like a jet
jockey.

Private planes just aren't powered for that sort of maneuvering. And what is
clean climb-out? It's about a 10° angle of attack, while your speed continues to

mount to the proper climbing velocity—90 mph—and you build up altitude—and safety.

Now comes the other thing most new pilots forget. The runway below has usually disappeared even though you've only used up half of it. In the fierce concentration of your takeoff, you've forgotten about the winds and the plane has slid or sailed sideward if there was a crosswind. The solution to the problem is simple: just keep on reminding yourself through the takeoff that you want to stay over the runway.

The rest of the takeoff is routine: keeping the climb attitude until reaching the standard left-turn altitude, 400 feet over the field; entering the turn level or close to level; and then departing the airport (if you are leaving) with a 45° turn to the right. There is one other important thing: keep your eyes open for other planes in the pattern. This is essentially a boring maneuver, time-consuming and wearying on the eyeballs, but a swivel neck will do wonders toward saving your neck.

Any time you're about ready to goof off on the job, shock yourself back into reality by telling yourself that the people in the other planes are blind, so that you have to do their watching for them, and your own as well. While this statement is not exactly true, there are enough characters who act like they are blind to keep you on your toes.

Once in a while try telling yourself that *you're* blind (which is what the guys in the other planes are thinking), and this will inspire you to be triply cautious. Better yet, take a friend along, not a girl friend, who you'll want to be looking at, but somebody you don't have to watch or don't want to look at, somebody you can tell without insult to keep his eyes open for other airplanes. Just be sure the somebody is a licensed pilot, since as a student pilot you can't take passengers. Your friend with his license is technically pilot-in-command, but for you it's good experience.

With the takeoff neatly done, and your flying (whatever it may be) also out of the way, next comes getting the airplane back on the ground. The first objective is to do so leaving the airplane and yourself in one piece. With the kind of airplanes built these days, this is relatively easy. It takes real talent to "prang" the airplane, as Air Force jet types put it, unless you're really trying.

The objective is to put the airplane on the ground *smoothly*—not by accident, but deliberately, so that you know *how* you did it—and begin building the insight, coordination and skill to do it over and over. No two landings are ever the same, as veteran pilots will tell you, but everyone keeps trying to make every landing the same—a *good* landing.

But this is perhaps slightly anticipatory. You may well discover that you're so fond of flying you don't want to land. Numerous types suffer from this character flaw. And it'll take a few times around to discover what this bit is all about. Sure you're fond of flying; why else would you have started to learn? It's just that you're not quite so fond of landing the airplane on what may be a tiny (but very adequate) airstrip which from a few thousand feet looks smaller than the lawn for a development home. The "I love flying, I don't want to land" line emerges as just what it really is: a transparent rationalization of fear, to get out of landing.

And if this affliction should strike you, there is but one answer: land the airplane. Not in a panic. But in stages. Flying the pattern builds your ability and

confidence and soon you'll no longer have any fear of landing. With each step correctly performed, it'll get easier. So do it just that way. Enter the pattern downwind in the correct 45° entry leg after checking the winds and traffic; fly the
downwind leg parallel to the landing runway correctly and then base leg and final
the same way. Control your speed, use your flaps and *set the plane up*. A few
times around like this are good practice and will get you over the fear of getting
back down to the ground. After the fear is at least understood, even if not overcome, then you'll begin to grasp what you're doing and how to actually land the
airplane.

The pattern.

Some of the more imaginative ad writers still are prone to spouting lines like
"You just drive it down" or "It lands as easily as a car drives." Don't you believe
it. Even if every airport had four miles of runway, so that you could taxi the
plane onto the ground, there would still be a wind to contend with. This is not to
say that the act of landing is ridiculously difficult; it *is* to say that it takes practice
and skill, and is a three-dimensional experience, as contrasted with the single-
dimensional act of driving a car.

No two student pilots ever land a plane in the same way. For some the act of
finding the ground is as easy as getting into bed at night. For others, it is a bouncing, annoyingly uncertain struggle like stumbling over a chair in the dark, and is
marked by rising pulse and blood pressure and wet brows.

When my wife, Joanne, took to landing, she did it as if she'd been doing it for
twenty years. Tom Jeffers, our instructor, watched in disbelief as she greased the
plane in, time and again, in perfect touchdowns, all executed in astonishingly
professional style. Then she gave up flying for a few months to have a baby and
when she came back to it there might just as well never have been a before, because she landed the plane so badly that no one watching could have believed
she'd ever tried it before.

Suffering from the "I've got to get it on the ground" complex, many of us pour the plane down on final and get it on the ground right away. Trouble is, it doesn't stay there. As in the movies, it touches down too hard and too fast, then bounces, careens and joggles down the runway—all in a perfectly straight line. And the harder you try to correct the problem the worse it becomes . . . until *you* know why. All of Tom's explanations, motions and demonstrations merely compounded the problem in my student days.

If I didn't pour it onto the runway too fast and bounce it, I'd flare out beautifully six feet above the runway. The plane would drop hard onto the blacktop, with the landing gear screaming in anguished protest against the punishment.

My logbook began to have a dismally familiar look with Tom's entries. It would read "T & Ls"—Takeoffs and Landings—"Just a few more needed," or "almost ready." You begin to feel as if it *is* a hopeless problem. Perhaps the answer would be to have somebody else along to land the plane, while I did all the flying. One pilot to fly and one to land.

Then two things happened. Tom suggested casually one day: "Stop looking out the front windshield all the time when you land. You see the ground all right, but looking ahead and down on it, approaching from a straight line, you have almost no real depth perception. Try looking out your side window for a second or so just before you flare out. That'll give you a better idea of exactly how high over the ground you are."

That seemed to help. Now when I bounced the plane I could watch the ground jumping up and down at me. But seriously, a strong idea of the plane's relative position to the ground began to form. My relative position above the ground struck home; this, of course, was the same as the plane's. Mysteriously, this began to work and landings began to improve. Yours will, too.

At about the same time, Tom, reviewing the landing problem, said for the eighteenth time: "Stop worrying about it. Remember all you're doing when you land is *stalling* the plane a few feet off the ground. Then try to stop the plane from landing—pull back on the wheel slowly—try to keep her flying." Something clicked inside my head and I knew in an instant that I had the problem licked.

With the natural fear we all have of stalling the plane anywhere, anytime, it made sense that I'd also be wary of stalling it—even just off the ground. Ridiculous, obviously, but I almost dragged Tom out to the plane to accompany me in another attempt at landing.

The next landing was as smooth as silk. And the one after that, and hundreds of others. Not all of them, of course. There have been, as there are for all men with wings, some deeply jarring experiences, bruising to the pride as well as to the lower spinal areas. But now I had it made. And your instructor will know it also, as he signs your logbook, declaring that you're ready to solo.

Flying at a 45° angle to your downwind leg, you enter the traffic pattern for your first landings. Establish your altitude at 800 feet above the terrain. If it is a field with a tower, identify yourself and your position: "Tri-Pacer One Zero Zulu entering downwind for Runway Two Four."

The downwind leg. You are flying parallel to the runway. Now is the time to locate your wind sock. Once you've established this, you go into the mechanics of preparing for landing. Carburetor heat is put on (some new planes state in the operator's manual that this is not necessary unless icing conditions are prevalent); check fuel, selecting the fullest tank; mixture should be full rich; if flying a plane with a controllable pitch propeller this is the time to adjust it; next cut back your throttle, apply back pressure and use trim to hold altitude while at the same time allowing the aircraft to slow fly. Some pilots will apply the first position of flaps on downwind, leaving less work for base and final.

Turning to base leg. As you turn, you begin to judge for wind, being careful not to drift too far afield. This is a 90° turn again.

Base leg. Now you begin to lose altitude. Judge how much flap, if any, you need to complete your landing. Play the plane to the wind. Here you may have to cut short or increase your leg's length to set up accurately for final.

Final approach . . . crossing the threshold. You are committed to land and now have the right-of-way over all other traffic. Final flap adjustment has been made, power is cut back unless you find a little extra necessary to get you to the spot you've picked to touch down. Now begins the work of "floating her in" gently, smoothly and safely.

Keeping the plane off the ground to shake off speed.

Now . . . the flare out . . . start pulling the nose up slowly and steadily.

TOUCH-AND-GO

The exact instant of touchdown.

The Tri-Pacer is barely touched-down before you put the carb heat in, use full throttle and start rolling for takeoff again.

Four feet off the ground – notice that the wings are almost flat with the horizon to get the speed up before climbing.

CLIMB-OUT

Speed has been built up; now you haul back for a safe climb-out.

Left wing into the wind to stop the plane from drifting off.

Clean climb-out.

Departing from the pattern in a clean 45° turn.

Chapter Seven. SHARPENING YOUR SKILLS: ADVANCED MANEUVERS

You'll spend many hours aloft at this stage of your training reviewing and practicing the air work we have just described. Like most overanxious students you'll have days when you treat your plane like no respectable plane should be treated. Your turns will be sloppy and your stickwork rough. You'll suffer too with each tortured bump of the landing gear when you flare out ten feet too high on landing and then wait in agony until the plane drops sickeningly to the runway.

You'll spend lesson after lesson going through preflight checks, takeoffs and air work until you'll feel that you've carved a special hole in the sky for yourself.

You'll suffer too through the many days when you want to fly and can't because of fog, early morning and late afternoon haze and smoke, poor visibility or low ceilings. On other days a bitter crosswind or turbulent air will keep you grounded. And you'll learn about the days of rough weather, when the agonized ups and downs imposed upon the airplane—and your stomach—will make landing and going home something to be grateful for. All these are a part of the experience of learning how to fly.

Soon, however, you'll move ahead into advanced air work, with your instructor demonstrating a large variety of turns from 180° to 720°, stalls, spin recovery and forced landings. If 90° and 180° turns had at first seemed easy, they soon become sheer torture as your instructor becomes more severe with your lack of precision. A 90° turn will mean just that, exactly 90°, not 92° or 89°.

If you are asked to do a 180° turn and don't come out over the spot precisely opposite from where you had started, don't expect praise. In 360° turns, if you lose as much as 50 feet of altitude you can plan on being chastised.

You'll soon plunge into 720s, which are quite simple, consisting of just making the same circle twice. You can't lose or gain more than 100 feet or deviate beyond reason from the 30° or 45° bank, but beyond this they are quite simple—to your instructor, that is.

You will probably pull the same thing all students do. After the first 360° turn is completed successfully, you feel so great that you promptly lose the hang of the thing during the second half, or worse still, the second time around, let your own propwash throw you. This offense indicates that you were so good you lost no altitude. A half-hour of this kind of idiocy is a good way to teach anybody to concentrate—unless they are incapable of experiencing dizziness after they've flown circles in the sky a few dozen times. Most students, after a good 720°, get careless on the pullout and manage to be sloppy about as simple a thing as recovering to level flight.

And then into 1080° turns—*three* complete circles without losing or gaining altitude. Somewhere, somehow, mysteriously, real skill begins to sink into you— and it isn't just because you do the same thing so many times that you automatically learn it. This is undoubtedly part of it. But there is much, much more.

The king-size holes you'll be boring into the sky will be complete turns around the compass, with the wind blowing from all quarters, full at it, quartering from all sides, and then away from it, trying to push up and pull you down beyond that 100-foot grace area. Naturally, you won't remain over any one landmark without allowing for the wind.

To do so you have to compensate with *steeper* banks when flying *with* the wind; and by *shallowing* them when flying *against* the wind, or you'll be carried away from your target below. But this is part of pylon turns, your next encounter. Suffice it to say that wind will begin to be a conscious thing that touches your hands on the ailerons after entering into your brains.

It permeates *all* the way—right down to the seat of your pants—which is exactly what it is supposed to do. Because you'll at least begin to grasp what seat-of-the-pants flying really means: knowing consciously inside your body exactly what you and the airplane are doing, and acting to correct errors before they get out of hand. Not at once will this realization come; but slowly, after many weeks, until it will be built up to the point where it suddenly will burst upon you.

If one word can sum up all that makes a good safe flier, it is *anticipation*— anticipating that in a 360° turn, you begin your pullout at 350°; anticipating that in a landing the wind may suddenly gust and get you in trouble unless you've figured out *ahead of time* what you'll do; anticipating *anything* that may happen.

And anticipating situations is nowhere more important than in the critical learning stages where you begin to acquire the insight, the skill and the outlook that will mold your flying habits through the years.

From those first seemingly complex 720s and 1080s, you'll move forward in your instructor's flight curriculum, which includes everything the FAA lists as necessary and a goodly number of items not listed at all. Some of them should be in it.

You'll begin flying *S* turns and elementary wind circles. In the *S* turn, you simply pick a straight road below, and flying 1500 feet over it, perform an *S* in the sky over the road, keeping all the elements of the *S* a constant distance over the road. You start the *S* turn by flying downwind or with the wind and crossing the road. Then turn into the wind—and here's the steepest part of the turn. As you come over the road in the middle of the *S,* you keep shallowing the bank, until when you're parallel with the wind you're flying with only a slight bank. Then into the second leg of turns over a highway and you feel absolutely nuts. Some of us are never able to perform this elementary maneuver properly, but can perform more complicated future workouts with no trouble at all.

When you fly a wind circle, you again pick a road, start your 360° turn over the straight stretch of the road and try to pull out at the same point where you had entered. With no wind it's a cinch. But when the wind is blowing against you, you end the circle up the road from where you began. Or, if the wind is coming from the side, you'll be off to one side of the road. The trick here is to adjust your angle of bank to try to compensate for the wind so that you end the circle nearly over the spot where you began it.

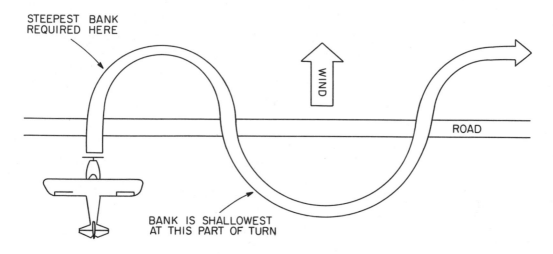

STEEPEST BANK
REQUIRED HERE

WIND

ROAD

BANK IS SHALLOWEST
AT THIS PART OF TURN

S-turns on a road.

Then on to pylon eights. You'll get to know two smokestacks, two houses, or two trees better than your own driveway. From 1500 feet you'll fly pylon eights around them, endeavoring to stay a set distance away while crossing up- and downwind.

If 1500 feet seems mighty low to practice pylon eights—which are the same thing as a figure eight and are also called eights-around-pylons—in the sky, remember this: if you get up much higher, the wind effect—the drifting of the airplane off course—will be that much harder for you, in the pilot's seat, to grasp in relation to the ground. Even big smokestacks get pretty small at 2500 feet.

Nothing in flying teaches you as much respect for the wind—and so develops your own critical judgment and feel of the airplane—as perfecting pylon turns. Entering the turn from straight-and-level flight, you will, with the plane flying perpendicular to the wind, first crab to windward to compensate for the drift effect, then roll into a steep bank so that the wind won't blow you too far from the smokestack. A third of the way through the first part of the turn, you'll lessen the bank, then roll out of it a bit more, midway through, until, when you are again at a right angle to the wind, you'll be back to straight-and-level flight. Then crab again as you cross the wind to prevent drifting off course.

Now you know your distance from the first smokestack and are committed to approaching the second stack as close to that distance as possible. The maneuver is repeated: the steep entry, then shallowing the bank, until coming out of it abeam of the wind you've reduced the bank to nothing to again compensate for drift.

If this doesn't seem to be difficult, you are right, it isn't—on a calm, windless day. But when the wind is roaring at you, really large bank corrections are necessary, with the bank sharply decreased on the windward side. It can get to be pretty discouraging on a gusty day, when you'll start the pylon with only a fair wind blowing, only to have the plane suddenly roll one wing up on you.

But this is part of the game. The same thing will happen on your approaches for landing, and the feel of the plane acquired here is exactly the right kind of training for anticipating correct approaches as when you're doing the real thing.

From the eights around a pylon, you move up to 720s around a pylon, which are considerably more difficult. Here you fly a tight circle around one point below, trying to keep the lateral axis—or the seat of your pants, if you will—directly above that point. The trick is to watch your instruments, learn them and let your *derrière* be a skyhook on the pylon. And all this while flying a set, key altitude, 1500 feet, which should not change but for a few feet.

After working through 720s around a pylon in all degrees of bank, from shallow to steep, your airmanship is honed to a fine edge. By this point, the objective is to be able to perform such a maneuver flying only by subconscious sense and conscious feel. We failed miserably in this goal at first, and you may too. But worry not: unless your friends were born with wings rather than arms, it is unlikely that they'll succeed right off the bat either.

Seven-twenties are a grueling skill test and there are also plenty of instructors unable to do them satisfactorily. With her left-turn pylons perfected, Joanne proceeded to the right-side pylons. Round and round she went, but she hit a snag, and was just not able to keep her wing glued to the pylon. The answer: she loosened her seat belt half a notch, so she was able to lean around Tom and finally see out the right window.

After the torture of pylons you'll get a breather and move into the maneuver we still consider the most satisfying—except for a really silken, smooth landing—spirals. Though this sounds like some kind of dangerous, twisting death maneuver, spirals are in reality little more than glides—circling down to another altitude while in a glide. The throttle is pulled back to glide rpm; the carburetor heat applied and then the airplane nose pointed down just a hair or two for good glide attitude.

The purpose: to lose altitude while staying within a given area—over your airport, for example. But the training maneuver is essentially to learn more about turning and banking while in a glide. The trick in a spiral, as in a glide, is to get the plane's nose attitude set up quickly for the proper airspeed and to keep it there; in most ships you set the nose angle down a hair with a little forward trim to maintain an 80-mph airspeed.

A good thing not to forget, by the way, is to clear the engine of the plane by increasing the rpm's every 15 seconds or so, just for a few seconds, . . . then bringing it back to glide rpm. Small-plane engines cool rapidly and "load up"; the smooth gunning of the throttle for a few seconds clears them out.

And in very cold weather it's a good idea not to cut below 1800 rpm's. The possibility of excessive cooling might mean that when you want to throw the throttle back, a misfire on the part of the engine could kill the whole thing. But this doesn't happen very often.

If spirals sound frightening, spins are enough to send anybody racing back home. The mere mention of the word is enough, thanks to the Hollywood film industry's treatment of spins, to bring the average beginner's blood pressure up to the danger point. Actually, spins are seldom a problem with modern airplanes. The stable high-lift wings on most light and business planes are spin-resistant. Any plane can be spun, but few modern craft can be spun unintentionally. It takes a really talented nut to spin a Tri-Pacer, any Cessna or most other new planes.

In the early days of aviation, when airplane design was more art than science, spins were a problem; so were the manufacture of reliable engines, instruments, and many other items that are now routine. But the scientists got into the act, thank goodness—specifically, the unsung heroes of the National Aeronautics and Space Administration (in those days the National Advisory Committee on Aeronautics, NACA)—and began studying airplanes in wind tunnels and experimenting with different types of wing designs.

Out of all this emerged scientific standards for the entire aviation industry. Even now, buried in the technical manuals of most airplanes, will be the note that the wing design is a NACA 112C, or some other number. This is as good as the government's approval of a new drug; it means that the wing design was painstakingly tested and, if properly applied to an airplane's design, it is a safe wing.

The problem nowadays is finding an airplane that can be spun. Most of them are specifically placarded, in the cockpit or operating manuals, *against* spins or aerobatics. They are planes built in the general light- or utility-plane category and are not stressed for weird and unusual maneuvers. They can be spun and, within limits, safely recovered. But they should not be. Not all of us are sharp enough to learn the limits. About the only planes still around that are capable of spins and other aerobatic maneuvers are the legendary Piper Cubs and the Aeroncas.

Spins are not even taught with light planes any more, nor are they required as part of the FAA's Private License flight test. Nevertheless, you will be a better pilot if you take the trouble to go up in a Cub one day with an instructor and get some spin recovery practice. We'll never forget in one of our earlier lessons how we accidentally almost dropped the Tri-Pacer into a spin.

Practicing stalls with Tom one fine afternoon, I'd hoisted the nose way up and in a moment of confusion had stupidly hit left rudder and right aileron. The old Tri-Pacer inwardly groaned, as if saying, *"No, no, not this,"* then shuddered in mid-air and began to break docilely into the beginnings of a spin. I had no idea what was happening until Tom snapped the controls away from me and recovered the airplane.

"Now," he almost screamed, "I have seen *everything!* They said it couldn't be done . . . that it was impossible to spin a Pacer . . . but you were about to." To this day, we all mutually groan remembering the incident. But I groan with inward satisfaction: I learned there and then what a plane about to enter a spin feels like; I might otherwise never have discovered this.

As for spin recovery, if you don't ever get into the Cub to learn, as you should, remember this much: the airplane's rotation—it looks like a maple pod whirling down to earth—is stopped by using opposite rudder and then lowering the nose to recover speed. The airplane in a spin is essentially falling in a stall, and rotating about its center axis.

Lest any or all of this worry you unduly, all light planes these days are built to recover from spins without the pilot doing a single thing. They're so stable that even the worst boobs get away with sloppiness.

As for stalls, you'll soon come to learn that they are the least popular, but nearly the most essential, of maneuvers to be learned. Everybody hates them because of the ups and downs your stomach does as it suddenly moves from a healthy angle of climb to an abrupt falling-out in a stall. There are power-on and power-off stalls, illustrating that the plane can be stalled even with full throttle if you are next to unconscious, or allow your climb-out on takeoff to get out of hand.

The basic maneuver is simple: in the power-off stall, carburetor heat is put on, you check the sky on all sides and especially below, then reduce power to about 1500 rpm. Bring the nose of the airplane up briskly (but not suddenly), until the plane runs out of airspeed—totters on the edge of being airborne—then "breaks" and falls in a stall. The nose will come up and up to what you consider an alarming angle, then drop down as the plane refuses to fly. To recover, you drop the nose sharply and apply power at the same time. The plane soon regains its flying speed.

Power-on stalls are entered in the same way, except that you do them with almost normal power—perhaps about 2200 rpm—and need no carb heat. The reason is to teach you that any plane can stall at any speed, from 50 mph to nearly its top-rated speed. And high-speed stalls have an element of danger, because things happen fast and violently; the ship will snap into the stall and recovery is more difficult. Important too is to know the "feel" of an oncoming stall, to know the sound of the engine as it approaches stall, and to know recovery procedure.

As your plane reaches its stalling speed, this is what happens: the smooth airflow around the wings is lost, since stalls are really caused by too great an angle of attack on the wings. As the smooth airflow is lost, turbulence of the air flowing past the upper part of the wings destroys most of its lift. Your plane is swiftly losing its ability to fly. When it does, it begins to fall earthward. The secret is always to release the back pressure—get rid of that high angle of attack in a hurry—the nose will scoot on down and the ship will regain its flying speed and attitude.

Stalls are mighty important. When they happen near the ground you may just not have enough altitude to recover before the plane hits the deck. Learning how to sense a stall—and thus how to avoid it—is as important a single item as you will ever learn about flying. Some ships have stall warning horns or buzzers, which will tell you when you're flying "on the edge of a stall." But the warning horn can fail.

Actually, most stalls take place where they should, when you are landing the plane; for that is really what a landing is—a clean stall just inches off the ground. But most unwanted stalls take place while the plane is turning—again because the ship will stall more rapidly in a turn than when you have it in level flight. And you'll remember why from earlier chapters: in the turn, the direction of your lift is no longer straight up and down from the ground, but has shifted somewhat to the side and tends to pull you to the side. To hold on to enough vertical lift for safety, you have to have more lift or, as noted earlier, *more power* —more throttle. And the steeper you bank, the more power you have to add. Remember this: keep turns moderate, especially near the ground, and you'll never get into a stall or into real trouble.

Another point never to confuse is this: a plane can stall in level attitude as well as when its nose is up. Lift is not created except with proper speed. And

POWER-ON STALL: Throttle at cruise power . . . wheel backward in maximum climb position, the Tri-Pacer darts upward. But as the angle of attack increases beyond the engine's ability to *pull* the airplane up, the airspeed drops out . . . 120 . . . 115 . . . 110 . . . 100 . . . 90 . . . 80 . . . 70 . . . 60 . . . 50 . . . and even at 49 mph (the Tri-Pacer's certificated stall speed with flaps off), until the plane hangs in mid-air, as if suspended from an invisible cable. One of the most stable and forgiving air platforms ever designed, the Tri-Pacer has been known to just outright *refuse* to stall . . . hanging almost motionless, but slowly losing altitude.

THE SECRET: The aircraft must be brought into the stall briskly, with a steadily increasing backward wheel motion, never hesitating. Since the stall maneuver disturbs the human sense of balance (and brings up unpleasant connotations to most of us), most student pilots tend to cheat the maneuver by *slowing* the rate of entry into the maneuver. Result: no stall or a stall that comes off so slowly as to fail to demonstrate the purpose of the maneuver, which is to instill unforgettably in the seat of your pants the *warning before the instant* when the plane will lose lift – its *controllable* motion – and fall out in a potentially dangerous maneuver. Knowing just when you are coming up to stall position can save your life.

instinct must be overcome in learning how to master stalls. The normal concept is to pull back on the wheel to increase back pressure, but this will only worsen the stall. As you learn, the instinct will go away and you'll acquire the habit of dropping the nose and applying power to recover.

In most modern planes that have flaps, the stall speed is somewhat increased when the flaps are in down position. The Tri-Pacer stalls at a speed 4 mph greater with full flap. The flaps actually add lift, of course. But when they are hauled up, the airplane may tend to drop because it has lost some lift. The natural and correct thing is to raise the nose—increasing the angle of attack— to hold on to your altitude. But if you happen to be flying near the stall speed, then raising the nose may project the ship into a stall.

A final word about stalls. They can happen above stalling speed—when a gust of wind socks the ship while you're on a landing approach, for example. The sudden wind change can cause your stall. The lesson is easy enough. When landing in gusty conditions, add some speed to your approach to give you better controllability and less chance of a stall.

It's the small things that many pilots do wrong, and few errors are more often committed unintentionally than skids. It is just as it seems—a skid is like that of an auto on an icy patch of road. Here's how it happens: if you hold too much left rudder in a left turn, the nose of the ship will swing to the left, or the inside of the turn, while the plane itself skids sideways toward the right, or the outside part of the turn. The skid is sloppy flying; you'll see it in the ball-and-bank indicator's failing to line up, or in the ball joggling crazily all around the place instead of being neatly centered. But the skid can also be dangerous. The plane's fuselage is hurled or forced against the airflow, creating greater drag and killing off airspeed, and the plane will begin to slowly lose altitude. Panic reactions have been known to take place, with the pilot pulling back on his wheel to hold onto his altitude—and pulling back so much that he hauls the ship up into a stall. If the plane is on its final approach, this may indeed be the *final* approach.

Skids are often confused with slips, which are seldom committed in error, and are a most effective way to kill off altitude when too high on a final approach. In the slip, the controls are deliberately crossed: right rudder would be held with left aileron, or left rudder with right aileron, but in moderation. The nose will then swing toward the outside of the turn, following the rudder, while the plane slips toward the inside of the turn and loses its lift much as it will in the skid. A real pro will often make his approach to a dangerous field deliberately quite high so as to clear obstacles safely, then will slip his ship in to a landing. Slips used to be routine in the days before flaps; now, with flaps, the same type of approach can be made while the plane is under safer control.

Along about this time in our training we abruptly became conscious of how fast or how slowly an airplane should be flown. Flying a short practice hop with Tom, we climbed out to 2500 feet, trimmed the ship and set her for cruise speed—2350 rpm. Only I didn't check the rpm gauge carefully enough because of another plane hovering too close to us. The gauge actually read 2450 rpm. The airspeed indicator sailed nicely through 120, past 125 and came to rest on 128 mph. The air had been moderately bumpy, but nothing to get upset about, as we flew along. All of a sudden the Tri-Pacer jolted violently, shot up several hundred feet and descended another few hundred just as rapidly. The airplane began bouncing up and down rapidly in the stretch of turbulent air. Bemused, I sat watching the airspeed gauge wondering what was happening when Tom, livid with rage, almost yanked the throttle out of the fire wall.

"If you want to take the wings off the plane," he hissed savagely, "do it on the ground with an ax—not in the sky." Jolted back to reality, I suddenly realized that the ship, while still bobbing around like a floating cork, was now doing its bouncing almost gently.

Until that moment we'd never known much about just what speed the ship *should* be flown at. Tom made sure that we never again lost track of it. Every airplane, like every man, has limits. The limits are clearly and concisely marked right on the outer dial of the airspeed indicator. They differ for every plane, but the same rules of common sense apply.

Never-Exceed Speed: No airplane should ever be flown beyond the never-exceed speed laid out in its operating manual. This is the maximum safe speed the plan can be flown at in *smooth* air. If you go to sleep and find the plane shooting through the never-exceed limit, *don't* panic and yank back on the elevators; if you do, chances are that you'll yank the elevators and wings off by imposing too great a load limit on them. Make the pullout smoothly and gently. Kill off your power first, then ease back on the wheel to drain off the rest of your build-up speed. The never-exceed speed on the Tri-Pacer is 170 mph; most light planes have a wide safety margin.

Maximum Cruising Speed: This is the greatest safe speed for moderate maneuvers in air that has become reasonably—but not violently—rough. On the Tri-Pacer this speed is 125 mph.

Maneuvering Speed: This is the speed we had exceeded in the past incident—the highest *safe* speed the plane can be flown at and still safely maneuvered in really turbulent air. Hitting turbulence at full speed is, for the plane's structure, like running into a brick wall. The trick is to reduce your speed the instant you know the air is rough and thereby reduce the strain on the airplane's body. In the Tri-Pacer, maneuvering speed is 83.3 mph. For most any airplane you can figure it at 70 per cent greater than stalling speed. To find this, multiply the stalling speed by 1.7. With the Tri-Pacer, multiply 1.7 by 49 mph. Result: 83.3 mph.

Flap Speed: If you ever just yanked on the flaps at full speed, you'd be torturing them with a load they were never intended to take. Flap speeds are the upper limits above which the flaps are never applied. In the Tri-Pacer, never apply the first notch of flap at higher than 95 mph; never put on full flap above 90 mph.

The speed-limit markings on the airspeed dial couldn't be more clearly marked. Never-exceed speed is blocked-out with a red line. Never-exceed speed and the normal operating speed are, additionally, separated by a yellow curved line. The normal operating speeds down to the stalling speed are marked with a green arc. And your flap speeds are laid out with a white line. You can be almost blind and still fly at safe speeds, as long as you're not *color* blind.

So the airspeed indicator in your plane tells you a great deal more than how fast or slow the plane is moving. And learning what other information it yields is one of the biggest safety factors in flying. The clue to following this simple instrument (located in the upper left-hand corner of the instrument panel in most planes) begins with the operator's manual of flight instructions that come tucked into a pocket in the plane.

Within its pages you will find and should study the specifications of the design and structure as checked by the FAA and approved for a certificate of airworthiness. Each airplane design has its own set of minimum and maximum operating factors and each plane has its own individual weight capacity. The method of stating this information is clear. As for our own Tri-Pacer: top speed, 141 mph; cruising speed (75 per cent power at sea level), 125 mph; optimum cruising speed (75 per cent power at 7000 feet), 134 mph, etc. That key includes flap speed, angle and rate of climb, and stalling speeds. These may seem to represent the performance ability of the plane. They do not. They are really guides to judging the performance ability.

Speaking of performance ability, it is about here in your flying—after you have mastered the advanced maneuvers and soaked up the basics of safety—that flying begins to become second nature. The gropings and hesitancy will be gone and in their place will come downright disgust with yourself every time you do any little thing wrong—such as flaring out six or seven feet in the air, all set for a perfect landing on that invisible runway that sits just above the real one for most new pilots. The answer is to get both runways in the same place at the same time before you break the landing gear or lose your nerve. Then you have it made.

Chapter Eight. HOW TO BE BRAVE DURING A SOLO FLIGHT

"All right, when?" you'll keep asking your instructor. "When can I solo?"

If he is like most instructors he'll reply with an enigmatic, "Who knows? Maybe never."

We can well remember our own impatience as the days and weeks of practice and more practice slipped by. Whenever we'd ask Tom, he ducked the question with a smile, saying, "Don't give it a thought, I'll let you know when you are ready. In the meantime, let's try a few more practice landings."

By then we knew that every rut and tire scrape on the runway belonged to us; we *put* them there, didn't we? When our friends would ask if we had our licenses yet, we'd try to impress them with just how complicated the entire business was. When we told them that we had over eight hours of flight time and were now on the threshold of soloing, some wise guy would loudly recall that good old Orville Wright did the whole thing in three hours, twelve minutes and six seconds. It got to be pretty hopeless.

Then one bright but windy and inauspicious day Tom took me out and began working me over as usual. A bit of air work and three landings. Then, as I started to taxi in from the last landing, he declared in his usual noncommital fashion, "Hold it here a minute." He got up, unhooked his seat belt, opened the door, started to get out and then, almost as an afterthought, said, "Take her around yourself. I can't stand it in here any more . . . not a minute longer."

Just like that, he was gone. Walking off the runway, lighting a cigaret, waving to me gaily. Sneaky, eh? All right, I thought, Who needs you?

One Zero Zulu wavered back and forth across the white line as it taxied back to the head of the runway. No other traffic was in sight. Just Joanne and a few characters pretending to look the other way next to the ops building, as if I were taking off on a suicide mission and they didn't want to say good-bye to the condemned. Curious, I mused, but somehow it felt like that to me too.

One Zero lined herself up nicely and headed off down the runway. A bounce here, and a bounce there, and she was airborne. Reaching 400 feet, I automatically looked to the right to check other traffic, and waited for Tom's usual "clear right" call. Nothing happened. My God! I thought. He's not here! I'd already started the bank for the turn when this realization hit me. Somehow I managed to keep right on going.

Up to 800 feet now. Pattern altitude. Who needs you anyway, Tom Jeffers? I asked myself. You do, idiot, a voice deep inside answered. I flew the downwind like a man under hypnosis. The base leg was beautiful and, fortunately, no other planes were around that I might have clobbered because I was now in a trance of determination. Then into the final approach. The first solo landing by now had been totally blocked out of my mind, except for Tom's noncommittal stare and wave-on as I went by alone.

Three takeoffs, three landings, I told myself. That's all I have to do. Then it didn't bother me any more. It became nearly routine, even though the right seat looked huge in its emptiness and the plane was a lonely place.

Each pattern was neater, each of the three landings better, and when I taxied up and shut the engine down, I knew I'd done all right.

Well, where is it? I asked myself. Where's the big thrill you're supposed to get? There was none. It was cool and windy and my shirt was soaking wet. And I was tired as all hell.

"Nice work," Tom commented. "Keep at it and one of these days you'll make a pilot." As he walked off with Joanne into the plane I gave him my dirtiest look and sat down exhausted.

"When is she going to solo?" I shouted after him. "We'll see," Tom hurled back. "Not today, anyway."

Ten minutes later, there he was, standing out on the runway alone, and Joanne was busy soloing. It was a snap for her, naturally. No nerves; no problems; just three perfect go-arounds and three neat landings. She walked out of the plane like she owned the sky. Not one sign of fatigue or doubt, all bravo. Months later she admitted what really happened. The second Tom closed that door she felt as though the key had been thrown away. Her first impulse was to taxi the monster off the runway. But there I was looking on, as well as Tom, and it was easier to face the controls than us. Putting her hand to the throttle, she took the leap. An eternity passed until she felt the wheels leave the ground. The strangest part of all, was that the entire time she was holding a running conversation with the empty seat next to her. Finally, in the downwind leg, with a free moment to realize what she had accomplished and a moment to look around, she found herself shrieking with relief, joy and most important the fantastic exhilaration of meeting adventure head-on. Now instead of dreading that first touchdown, she accepted it . . . accepted it in order to be off again to the new challenge of the sky.

We all had a cup of coffee and exchanged critiques and questions while Tom signed our logbooks.

"Well," Tom declared with relief, "I never thought we'd get *that* out of the way. Now we can begin to teach you something about flying."

Weeks later, after he'd worked us over again on everything—from air work through landing full circle—his words came back to haunt us. It was all too true. The solo hardly matters. It is kind of a hurdle—but only for the student pilot. It's something he has to get out of the way for his own pride and respectability. For the instructor, it is a mere formality. Sometimes they'll get it out of the way just to build up the neophyte's confidence. This is not to say they'll let anybody who's unprepared go up alone. But it becomes so vital psychologically to the student that he be allowed to solo, that he begins to learn less for a while until he is cut loose and sent out on his own.

So the solo has to be gotten out of the way. Then most instructors go back to dual instruction with you—polishing, correcting, setting you straight—while at the same time letting you gradually begin to build up your solo time. And suddenly you're absorbing much more, learning faster, flying far better. The solo is the mark of acceptance. After soloing, the student pilot is allowed to fly by himself and to practice as much as he wishes.

If the bird is ever going to be turned loose on his own, he has to convince himself that he can fly. Now you'll be at least partially convinced, and ready to move on to the point where flying really becomes fun.

Those first few weeks after your first solo flights are one long dare—at least they were for us. The actual solo had been a snap. But the next day, coming out to the field, making ready to go up without anyone in the right-hand seat was far more frightening. It is for most of us. You can hardly believe that it was you who ever did the job. I should qualify the "most of us" as being mostly men. For not so, apparently, with the weaker sex. Joanne blithely waved so long, and five minutes later was airborne, carefree and having a ball. My preflights looked more like the FAA certification tests on a new aircraft than an ordinary ground check.

The script went like this: 8 A.M. Arrival at Teterboro—no one was there yet. 8:15 A.M. Grumbling line boy arrives, produces key for the airplane. 8:20 A.M. The discovery that, as usual, the plane hadn't been gassed the night before and is one quart low on oil. This somehow makes you suspicious of the whole business. 8:30 A.M. The plane is gassed, oil-checked, preflighted. 8:35 A.M. Gave the line boy the third degree about the plane's rough idling, loading up when carb heat is applied, and anything else that seems appropriate. 8:36 A.M. "Look, I only put gas in . . . I don't know anything about what goes on *inside* the engine."

8:37 A.M. Checked the weather. This is vital, particularly when the sun is shining brightly, there's hardly any wind, and you're not planning to go more than five miles from the airport. 8:39 A.M. Taxied out—there's not another plane on the field since it's Sunday morning and only real maniacs like you would get up at 6 A.M. to go flying. Just to be ornery, you run through the entire run-up twice and still can't find anything wrong with the engine.

8:41 A.M. Cleared by the tower to take the active and take off. Then spent 30 seconds making sure the nose wheel is glued to the white line. Since this is only 29 seconds longer than needed, you ignore the Tower's cry, "One Zero Zulu cleared for takeoff! One Zero cleared . . . One Zero . . . Do you *read* Teterboro tower?" (After this has happened twice, you get to practice the fine art of having the plane rolling *before* the tower manages to finish "One Zero Zulu cleared.")

By then you work up a new gambit. As soon as the tower has cleared you and you're rolling, you dramatically pick up the mike and intone, in the best Air Force style, as practiced by mannered B-52 pilots: "One Zero Zulu rolling *now!*" I never could quite figure out the need for this, except at night, since the tower could quite clearly see that I was rolling unless they were blind. At any rate, it succeeded in producing large quantities of respect from Teterboro's overworked and jittery tower men.

8:42 A.M. Airborne, and you break out of the pattern into the magnificently quiet world of New York on a Sunday morning. There's not a plane in the sky.

Down with all instructors: now I can fly by myself.

LaGuardia, Idlewild and Newark are sleeping giants; down below, the parked
707s, DC-8s, 880s and 990s haven't as yet loaded up and headed out, screech-
ing, for the runways. This is your world! The earth people are sleeping; the
multi-engine monsters are silent; hardly a car stains the network of confused
highways below. Thousands of acres of free land and sky belong to you alone.

8:43 A.M. Course 020°. Heading northward up the Hudson, the favorite
Sunday morning air-constitutional. Over the Teterboro practice area, near Wood-
cliff Lake and the Oradell Reservoir, you practice self-consciously, wondering
about what anybody below thinks if they are watching. For those first few months
it is tentative exploration—feeling the air out and building up nerve. No sudden
maneuvers. You need quiet, the steady droning of the engine to convince you
that all is really well, and time to build up your confidence that the aircraft will
keep on flying. But from simple 360s and 720s I work into all manner of
pylons, complicated patterns and approaches that no one had ever taught me.
They were my way of flying and, though they proved nothing, they gave me a sense
of freedom of expression; I was doing something I wanted to.

Then into spirals, glides and shooting steep pull ups. All the while I kept
dreaming of the day when I'd get the courage to do stalls alone. Finally, one
Sunday, I couldn't put it off any longer and went off on a wild orgiastic burst
of stalls; after eight of them I no longer feared a stall and I quit.

8:59 A.M. Flying at 2000 feet up the Hudson, One Zero Zulu shoots past
the Tappan Zee Bridge and prepares to strafe cabin cruisers on the river. After this
Walter Mittyish daydream, I drone on northward, past the Victory Fleet, head
inland over West Point and then warp in the wind past the bend in the
Hudson toward Poughkeepsie.

9:12 A.M. Shooting through the pass between the two 2500 foot mountains
on the approach to Poughkeepsie, I meet a lonely Cessna 172. He's flying down
below at about 1800 feet and I'm up at my standard 2500 feet. There is no exchange of wing-rocking, nor a friendly cry of hello on Unicom. Neither of us is
willing to shatter the protective, soul-wrapping peace of the Sunday morning.

9:20 A.M. The Poughkeepsie low-frequency range passes beneath me, and the
signal on my set swells accurately. I then crank in Poughkeepsie Omni-Range,
and line up the ship. Visibility is at least 15 miles; no need for VOR (Very High
Frequency Omni-Range), but I like to keep the set on as a continual cross-
check, letting the reassuring bleep-bleep of the code signal run through my ears.

Somewhere back there, 60 miles to the south, is a concrete cell called an
office in a steel-and-brick jungle that is called a city. In less than twenty-four
hours, I will rejoin the condemned, but for now I've escaped and for every mile
I put between the Tri-Pacer and New York I feel better.

9:26 A.M. I circle Dutchess County Airport, call them on Unicom and a
sleepy gal answers: "Runway 24 . . . wind southwest at 15." Still no other airplanes. Dutchess County is a beautiful airport with dual cement runways out in
the open and only a few score planes attached to it. Seldom is there much
traffic; for that reason, it's a favorite cross-country and landing practice airdrome.
No flaps; I let the Tri-Pacer fly herself in and calmly roll-out.

9:32 A.M. After a cup of coffee, I take off, letting the Tri-Pacer build up
a walloping 75 mph, and then zoom off the ground in a steep climb. Unneces-

sarily assertive, but deeply satisfying. I set course for Danbury Airport, some 40 miles to the southeast, and decide to climb up a bit, to see what the Tri-Pacer will do. The air is moderately warm and the climb is a long, slow procedure.

9:41 A.M. I'm climbing on an almost due easterly heading and it never occurs to me that I'm breaking right through one of the main airways to LaGuardia. Far off to the north, I see a speck, then another. Dust on the windshield obviously. But the specks grow. I'm still climbing. They're still growing. But no worry, they look like they'll pass far above me.

It never occurs to me that they might be descending. Next time I look, one speck is only about two miles off; the second may be four miles. The thought hits me like a thunderbolt at the same instant I recognize the first plane as an American Airlines Electra; he's letting down into LaGuardia and I'm climbing—it's just possible we could meet in an angry clash of metal and fabric that will be the first and last meeting for us both. And that is what very nearly happens.

He's less than a quarter of a mile off when I act. I haul the Tri-Pacer up into a steep climbing turn to the right while he steepens his descent and banks to the left. I can almost see the angry stare of the co-pilot. That must have made several friends for private flying. I make a mental note never to indulge in long climbs or descents that'll take me through air lanes. Fortunately, it was a CAVU (ceiling and visibility unlimited) day and we saw each other in time. But I remember the FAA statistics; *most* mid-air collisions take place not on low-visibility days, but on just such dreamboat days, when everybody sits back fat, happy and stupid.

9:59 A.M. My altimeter reads 11,500 feet and the Tri-Pacer is clanking along on all four cylinders. I'm right over Danbury and feel like a fly in outer space. Time to go down. I pull out the carburetor heat and notice with some amusement that the rpm's pick up by about 100 beats—there had been a shade of ice in the carburetor.

Throttle back now; the plane falls beautifully silent and down we go. With the Tri-Pacer's 7:1 glide ratio, I could make it from here almost into Westchester, but not quite close enough to the airport to put the glide-ratio figures to a safe test.

The descent from 11,500 feet seems to take forever; I recover with power and break into the pattern at Danbury. But now the wind has picked up and is bumpily pouring over the hills surrounding the airport. Downwind. Then base and onto final, no need to stop here. I jolt the Tri-Pacer into another of those embarrassing landings, shove the power back in and keep right on moving in a touch-and-go.

10:20 A.M. I cross the Hudson north of the George Washington Bridge, and the solitude of the morning is gone. The air is alive with weekend fliers, Sabrejets from Westchester County (no longer present) screaming through the sky, and all manner of commercial traffic choking the air over the New York area. The familiar smoky dank haze rises off the Jersey meadows and Teterboro lies clothed in its usual dirty soot.

10:25 A.M. Teterboro looks like a flea circus in a smoke-filled tent. At least thirty private planes cavort around the area—in the pattern, out of the pattern, in between the two steps, and a few, for good measure, who only think they're in the pattern. The man in the tower has that all-too-familiar choking sound of sheer desperation in his voice "*please* keep the pattern in close!" as he tries to keep up with too many calls for landing instructions, too many departure requests and, to compound his work, a couple of characters reporting that they're passing over the airport at 3000 feet.

10:31 A.M. A perfect bounce onto Teterboro's blacktop. But only one bounce. A pouring crosswind made it interesting; it was a sideways bounce—the plane moved at least three feet to the east between the first and second time it contacted the ground. But no sweat; she was under control, albeit somewhat dubiously.

That was the way it went, Sunday after Sunday, and on the few afternoons when I could get to the airport in time for a few go-arounds. Many of us do most of our flying on weekdays. It doesn't really matter when as long as you're learning the air in your own way, building up the solo time you need for your license and acquiring the confidence you have to get before it all became easy enough for it to be fun.

Some Sundays it would be just "around the pattern for an hour"; the weather wouldn't be good enough to go anywhere, or there wouldn't be time enough. But mostly we both preferred to flee to outlying airports on short cross-country hops. In less than six months we'd been to every one of them we cared to go to, as well as to quite a few we hadn't cared to visit but felt it kind of important to learn about and test our skill on.

The magic spell of Sunday mornings has never been broken. You *must* get out early, while the air is still, silent and cool and the dew still lies in cool drops on the wings. The drum-banging voices do not exist; they might never have been for all it matters after a few minutes, when you are united as one with a machine that is responsive, friendly, trustworthy and *flies*.

Alone—or with a friend who can sing silently in the unbroken caress of the atmosphere while the wing slices through air that still flows smoothly even on a hot summer morning.

The only problem is getting up early. Now who can ever manage to get to bed at a decent hour on a Saturday night? We may all be sleepy birdmen, but we always fly.

Chapter Nine. HIGHWAYS IN THE CLOUDS

You feel aloneness. You've soloed now and know the stabbing fear of being alone in a cockpit for the first time with no one's hands on the wheel but your own. One hand on the wheel, the other on the throttle; one seat full, the instructor's empty. For us One Zero Zulu had looked frighteningly big, and we had both felt helplessly small. But we had each conquered the fear—as you can and will —and made that circuit of the field three times, taking off, landing, as your instructor watches intently from the grass. The fear will disappear, and in its place comes the exhilaration of mastering the plane. Then suddenly watching other student pilots solo, realizing just how little it means—taking off, doing a pattern around the field, landing safely.

Flying is much more than that. And once you solo, no one needs to explain in any detail that the real work and fun lie ahead—in learning navigation and cross-country flying.

Now begins the work, with unexpected questions and sudden maneuvers—getting ready for cross-country flying. To move up a notch—that very big notch to earn your private pilot's license, enabling you to carry friends or family in your plane and really use it—you have to qualify for cross-country flying, as well as to pass a three-hour written examination and a flight test.

The Federal Aviation Agency rules call for seven hours of dual cross-country flying with an instructor, and ten hours of solo cross-country—including four trips of 25 miles or more from your home airport and one round trip of 200 miles or more from home base. Landing at each airport, you have to get your logbook signed (anyone there will do) as proof that you have really completed the flight. Don't be too embarrassed to ask after landing (even a sloppy landing). People at airports can pick out a solo student on his first cross-country flight blindfolded, and are always obliging as well as sympathetic. But before you take that step alone, your instructor must sign your logbook "okay for cross-country," and before that you have to prove you can find your way home.

Those first voyages away from home become a test not only of your ability in flying the plane, but of your knowledge of navigation, radio use and weather. But most important, they are to test your confidence in yourself.

There are three navigational methods to learn, the three nearly all pilots use:
Dead-Reckoning—or finding your way by using landmarks such as highways
    and towns.

Pilotage—finding your way with compass, aerial maps, computer and watch.
Radio Navigation—using the nationwide network of omni-range stations and the
    low-frequency radio ranges to guide you. More about omni later. It's one
    of the greatest boons aviation has ever had.

All three methods are now essential for flying in this country. Starting off on
your first cross-country flight, you'll usually use pilotage and dead-reckoning.
These will test your basic navigational ability—reading a map, learning the
effect of the wind on your course and ground speed, finding how to compute
ground speed and airspeed and wind angle, and estimate fuel consumption and
time of arrival at your destination.

All of these seem complex and puzzling, doubly so because you'll find your
head filled with the mounting uncertainty of first flight alone away from home.
Though eager to be done with it, you will still be leery of jumping into it for
fear of getting lost. The means of escape becomes a challenge, but a challenge
you will soon learn to keep in perspective. You don't go until you understand all
the essentials. And don't try to convince an instructor that you're ready; let him
do the deciding.

If wiseacres kid you (and some always do), just remember that if you are lost
on the ground, you can pull off the highway onto the grass and wait for someone
to come along. Lost in the sky, *you alone have to find where you are.* There's
no one up there to show you the way to go home but yourself. And instead of
the grass to pull off on is an airfield, or a farm field, which may be out of reach.
Ask the wiseacres what *they* did.

Before the first dual cross-country flight it is well worth your time to arrive
a bit early to have a final word with your instructor. Sit down and review
with him the basics of plotting a course learned in ground school—and be sure
to know enough to benefit from the flight, so that you won't get upstairs and just
fly for fun.

The morning of our first dual cross-country, the three of us sat down at a
large table and spread out the sectional aerial chart of the New York area, which
covered both our home base and our destination for this first short hop. The
map looked complex enough for plotting a course to the moon, not just for a
hop of a few miles. And the back side, explaining how to use it and all its
markings, made us feel utterly ignorant. Joanne cracked that it was just like
picking up a French cookbook before she learned how to read French. The map,
once understood, laid out our highways in the clouds and contained its own
road signs and markers.

There are eighty-eight of these sectional aerial charts (or SACs for short),
which cover the entire United States. For longer hops, there are world aerial
charts (or WACs); sixty-two of these cover the country. The SACs use a scale
of eight miles to the inch; WACs cover sixteen miles to the inch.

The first few cross-country hops should be easy, so pick out a comparatively
short flight and build up your own confidence and skill at the same time, and
then gradually work into longer, more difficult flights.

A flight around fifty miles for a first try makes sense. A flight to Dutchess County Airport at Poughkeepsie, New York, from Teterboro in New Jersey would be approved by any instructor. The course, as you can see on the chart, parallels the Hudson River most of the way. The Hudson is one of the finest landmarks you can find in the crowded eastern states, where city unfolds into city, and factory meets factory, with little open land in between, making really good landmarks few and far between.

Course diagram on New York chart.

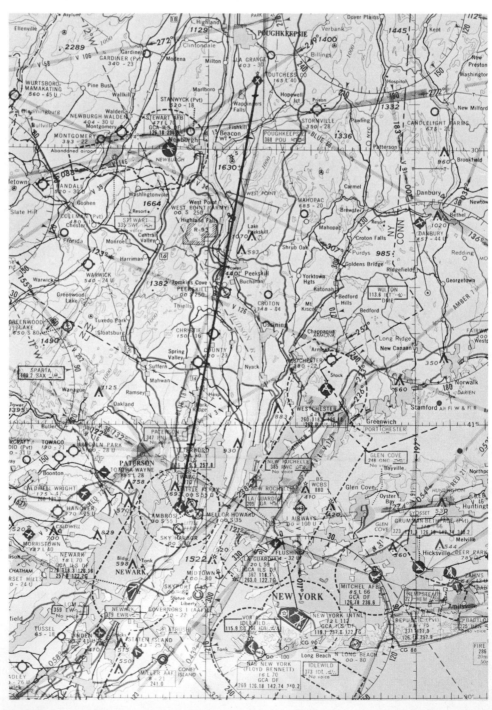

Dutchess County Airport has good hard-surfaced runways from 3400 to 4000 feet long. It's not a good idea to pick grass or soft-surfaced fields with short runways on the first few hops. If it's raining hard, or a gusty wind is blowing, there might be some trouble getting onto or off the field. But it is important to know how to use short fields, and to practice short-field landings (for your license, you have to be able to put the plane down within 300 feet of a specified position). However, early cross-country flights are not the time to try short-field landings.

To establish your course, rely upon your protractor-plotter—a combination ruler and semicircle with points of the compass marked on it and a mileage scale. There are a number of these sold (we use the Weems Mark II, which is inexpensive—two dollars—and simple to operate). On the ruler side of the plotter, draw a straight line from Teterboro Airport through Dutchess County Airport. Then turn the protractor side up, and place the center hole over the meridian or longitude line that runs closest to midway of your course (they run down and across all aerial charts). Lining up the upper straight edge with your line from airport to airport, and with the hole over the meridian line, read your true course off the protractor: 12°.

An easy mistake is to read it backwards, finding the reciprocal—or the inverted course—your return heading, 192°. It has to be wrong, since 12° is almost due north, and 192° is almost due south.

Then look up at the top of the chart where, at each longitude line, the amount of magnetic deviation—caused by variations in the earth's magnetic field—is clearly marked in red. (Longitude lines are in blue.) These deviation markings are called isogonic lines. They run across the entire world. Near the center of the United States, east and west isogonic lines meet. There, the deviation is nonexistent—0°. But spreading out east and west the deviation increases. The area you now have charted through is in the 12° west zone—meaning a magnetic course of 24°. There's an easy rule, an old flier's rhyme, "East is least, west is best." Subtract for an easterly variation, add for west.

This establishes the magnetic course of 24°, but now still to be reckoned with is the wind. This is a good time for a coffee break and a call to the nearest flight weather station, in this case the one at Newark Airport. Surface winds are reported at let's say 270 (degrees) at 20 (miles per hour); winds aloft (at your flying altitude) were running the same. With a simple pilots computer or by recalling our lessons in figure eight and pylon turns, you can see that the strong wind from the west will push us to the right of our course, unless we compensate by steering more to the left.

After this, you know your drift angle (the way the wind will be pushing you), and now you are able to work out your ground speed—how fast you will actually be moving over the ground below.

Airspeed, as opposed to ground speed, is just as it seems, the speed of the airplane through the air. Ground speed is your true speed—the rate at which you are covering miles over the earth.

The difference is basically the wind: you almost always fly in a wind. Either it is pushing you from behind (the friendly tailwind), or holding you back by blowing from straight ahead (that old devil headwind), or pushing from one side or the other (a crosswind). Mostly the wind is a combination of crosswind with tailwind or headwind, since you seldom fly directly into or ahead of a wind.

When a plane is flying into a 20 mph wind at 120 mph, the ground speed would be only 100 mph. But, with that 20 mph wind on its tail, it'd be scooting along at 140 mph. The airspeed indicator on the dash still reads 120 mph regardless of the wind, but the speed is actually greater or (as is much too often the case) not as high as on the indicator.

On the map now is the drift angle, and ground speed. The indicated airspeed would come off the dash. Then, simply add or subtract for temperature and altitude. Airspeed goes up two per cent every thousand feet, as the atmosphere thins out, offering less resistance to the aircraft. If you are going 100 mph at 1000 feet, you will be doing 120 mph at 10,000 feet—20 per cent greater. But relax; the temperature variation isn't a major consideration for speed calculation in your kind of flying.

From the flight weather report you know that to hold your course you must crab, or angle the plane ten degrees into the west, so that the westerly wind will not blow you too far off course to the east.

The last thing to figure is compass deviation—the actual error of the instrument in your cockpit. All compasses err to a certain extent. The compass card above the instrument—which is regularly calibrated—tells the amount of deviation. It will, for example, tell you: for north 360, steer 358; or for 60°, steer 65°. You know that your true heading is 24°—now simply add the 2° correction—steer 26° or, after allowing for the wind, 16°.

Now that you've gone through it all, cross-check and retrace your steps—play safe. It looks like this:

True course	12°
Magnetic variation (12° west)	+12°
Magnetic course	24°
Compass deviation (plus 2°)	+ 2°
Compass course	26°
Wind-drift angle	−10°
Actual course (compass heading)	16°

Now, planning a cruising altitude of 3500 feet to Dutchess County, the altitude —adding 2 per cent every thousand feet—would add seven miles an hour to your True Indicated Airspeed or TIAS. It would now be 132 mph. There's an all-important rule to remember in planning courses: Again and again ask yourself, DOES IT MAKE SENSE? Obviously (and this happens to veteran pilots as well as to beginners), if the course you plan calls for 60°, and by looking at the map you can see it's more like 90°, you have erred somewhere.

One pilot we know flew from Teterboro to Pittsburgh on the wrong compass heading all the way. He got there, too—on a bright, clear day—because he followed landmarks (using dead reckoning) instinctively, rather than his compass. This character is just a born scout; but Lord help him when the earth below is swallowed up in haze and there are no landmarks to follow. Only once have I started to fly the wrong heading; luckily, I have a friend I fly with who is such a fine pilot that he merely looked at me without saying a word and I knew instinctively I'd done something wrong. (If it takes a second look for me to grasp an error, his face contorts in pain and starts to writhe in mock agony; it's never taken a third look, though I've been tempted to try just for fun, but I've always feared he'd just plain collapse.)

So the moral is clear: always recheck and straighten out the boggle on the ground. Instructors, and everyone else in aviation, respect the pilot who freely admits and corrects his errors. Good pilots want to be right; those who don't correct errors never get to be good pilots and seldom get to be veteran pilots.

There is still another use of the plotter. It has mileage scales for all kinds of aerial charts. On this you figure your total distance—52 miles—and then draw light lines about every ten miles on your course. These will be the approximate places to look for good checkpoints. Most of the time you won't find good checkpoints conveniently placed every ten miles; they may be fifteen or twenty miles apart. It doesn't matter how far apart they are, just as long as they're clearly visible regularly from the air. Then simply add the extra mileage between points and figure accordingly.

Checkpoints tell you, when you look at your watch or dashboard clock (which you start and note the time on when you take off), exactly how many miles you have covered in how many minutes—and most important—if you are on course. For example, if you have been in the air ten minutes and your plane is flying at 120 mph, then you would have covered 20 miles. If your 20-mile checkpoint doesn't appear below within another minute or two don't just keep going; circle the area until you find yourself on your map.

The checkpoint will also tell you how fast your actual ground speed is; simply divide the time you've been in the air (ten minutes in this case) into the number of miles you've covered (20 miles) and you come up with your ground speed (120 mph).

And another clue—how to judge crosswinds in the air. You pick two prominent landmarks right after taking off and fly between them on your compass heading. By the time you've reached them you'll be able to tell whether the wind is blowing you to the left or right of your course. (Make sure they are immovable objects. Joanne picked a large freighter in the Hudson once that she was sure was anchored; not until she got over it did she notice its wake and then she was a couple miles off course.)

The next step is to figure fuel consumption. A Tri-Pacer carries 36 gallons of fuel and burns about 9 gallons an hour. Since the flight was only 104 miles round trip, there would be more than enough fuel in the tanks. But nevertheless figure out fuel consumption. Start right and make good habits that you intend to keep. If you run out of gas in a car, the last asthmatic cough of the engine may be disturbing, but you simply pull off on the shoulder of the road. Running out of gas in the air is the most unforgivable sin one can commit in flying, and too frequently one's last as well as one's first. But people keep right on doing it—they seem to expect to find a gas station on Cloud Nine. The stories are unbelievable. One four-wheel jockey, who apparently thought the AAA was right behind him with a tanker plane, flew from New York to Greensboro, North Carolina, never once looking at his fuel gauge. He made a perfect three-point landing in the trees at the head of the runway after his engine died—a victim of acute fuel starvation.

If, at this point, you are completely overwhelmed by all the figures, nevertheless you now know how you are going to navigate to a given destination. No fair, this time, using omni-range—this makes it too easy to find the airport. These first few cross-country trips are to learn pilotage and dead reckoning, nothing else.

Omni, a vast network of Federal Aviation Agency stations sending out very high frequency radio signals in a 360° radial, makes it possible for any pilot to find his way to and from a station with no ground reference. Commercial and military pilots seldom fly anything but omni, but they had to learn pilotage, too. A station can always break down or, more likely, the radio in the plane can blow a tube. Also, the omni may not be a direct route to your destination, and you'll want to or have to fly by pilotage.

Learning to fly omni without first learning pilotage is like learning to drive a car before learning how to walk. And there are other radio aids aside from omni: the low-frequency radio range stations and the directional loop on your plane, or ADF (Automatic Direction Finder) which enables you to "home-in" and find your way using the signal from any radio station. These radio aids will be dealt with in the next chapter.

All this paper work will, for the first few cross-country flights, take about an hour; experienced pilots do it in far less time. But, as Tom commented on our first pre-cross-country trip, watching us throw away the heaped-up scraps of paper, after combining everything on one sheet, more experience meant less investment in paper.

The course just plotted was the one I took. Joanne and I walked out to the Tri-Pacer with a new respect for the science of flying—which, as we had now learned, involves more than simply the art of flying a plane. Flying is both art and science: meteorology, navigation, radio and engineering; blended with man's own art—his skill in controlling his plane—to make the entire business surer, safer, easier and more fun.

Tom followed us around as we went through the preflight check of the plane and its engine. The preflight check is another rule of the air; it takes only a few minutes but may prolong your life many years, as well as add immeasurably to your own confidence. You know the plane is all right before taking off. One less worry.

Traffic at Teterboro was light and we were cleared for takeoff in barely more than the few minutes it took us to run-up the engine and go through our cockpit check. The Tri-Pacer skipped down the runway and jumped into the air, which was gusty, making this first cross-country trip more piloting work.

After I broke out of the Teterboro traffic pattern in a broad overlong 30° climbing turn, I felt Tom's disapproving glance on me. He quietly said, "You added another few minutes to the trip by not making the bank sharper and getting on course right away. You don't need a 65° bank to do it, but do it cleanly and quickly." Like most beginners, I'd loafed through the turn and loafed getting on course, and then was unable to understand why the plane took so long getting us to our destination.

It was a typical New York City day: hazy, with a high overcast, and enough ground smoke and dust to cut the predicted seven to eight miles of visibility down to three to four miles. I jealously thought of flying out in the West, where visibility was often 50 to 60 miles. Three to four miles was good enough today for VFR (Visual Flight Rules) flying, and excellent for a *dual* cross-country plane trip. It makes you work to find all your landmarks and checkpoints, which is as it should be. But on your first solo cross-country, make it a good day. Tom warned us of this, again mostly for our own confidence.

As we lined up our course heading—16°—we carefully picked out two factories dead ahead just six miles past the airport. We soon found that the wind was not as strong as forecast; by steering 20°, we were able to hold our course.

Our first checkpoint, Oradell Reservoir, to our right, passed by right where it should have been. At this point, I felt a little like Columbus; I'd managed to find my own way for 8 whole miles. We looked at the watch; we'd covered the 8 miles in 4 minutes; we were making 120 mph, not as fast as we'd figured. It was the wind again; it had swung more to the north—a headwind.

Checkpoint two also ticked by beautifully—Lake De Forest, in Rockland County, a three-mile-long finger-shaped body of water that stands out clearly from the air. The Hudson River, to the east, was barely visible, though it was only two and a half miles away. Time: 11 minutes to checkpoint two—still traveling at 120 mph.

Checkpoint three was the bend in the Hudson River at Tomkins Cove. The only trouble was that it had moved slightly to the west; we were east of the river. Ridiculous, of course, since the river hadn't moved; we had. I shot a look at the compass; I was steering 30°. Fascinated by my great navigation, I'd neglected the real navigator, the compass. So I turned left quickly, getting back to course. But I had gone nearly two miles off course, losing time; and getting back again took more time.

Checkpoint four, a mile east of the river near Peekskill (and this time meant to be there), wouldn't have been easy to find but for the river. It was really nothing more than a small stream curved in a U-shape, not easily visible from the air, and a set of railroad tracks to the west of the stream. It looked like enough on the map, and it was enough, if you watched closely so as not to lose it. But in bad weather it would have been impossible to find. The moral is clear: pick a checkpoint you can hardly miss, not one you can barely find.

Checkpoint five was the town of Wappingers Falls, and since it was due south of the airport, and only three miles away from it, it was easily located. We could see Dutchess County Airport clearly; visibility had picked up, as it does away from all big cities and industrial areas, when you leave the smoke and soot behind.

I eased back on the throttle, beginning my letdown. The Tri-Pacer's nose dropped and the earth came up to meet us as the wind played the strings in the struts to the accompaniment of our 160-horsepower bass section. Clearing myself

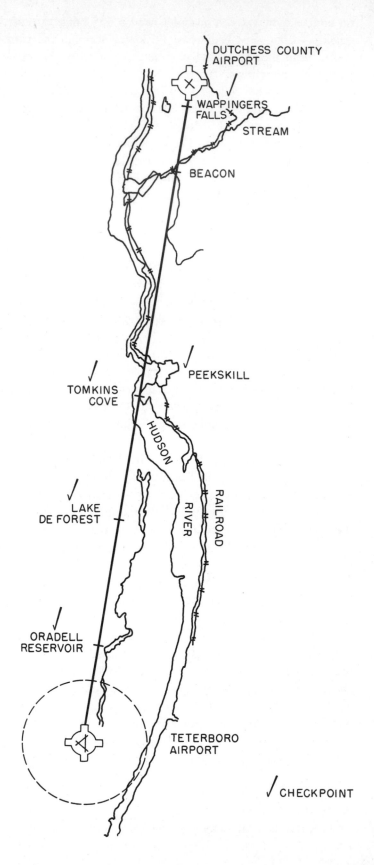

Checkpoints.

Omni-range station under the Tri-Pacer. Not only is it more accurate than a road sign – you can find it when you *can't* see road signs.

The Victory Fleet moored in the Hudson River near Tomkins Cove. If all checkpoints were this good, you wouldn't have to work at all. . . .

Downwind for runway 24 at Dutchess County Airport – one of the cleanest and best laid-out in the United States.

Banking to line up the Tri-Pacer for runway 24 on our final approach at Dutchess County. Don't ask how I ever took the picture and landed at the same time: I still don't know.

in a series of gliding turns, I shook off altitude, preparing to enter the airport's
traffic pattern.

Dutchess County Airport has no tower, but it does have Unicom (the pilots' universal radio frequency) and, when I called in, I got a prompt reply with advice on winds, runway and traffic direction. Following Tom's advice again, I flew over the airport (at 1500 feet, well above traffic) and checked the wind sock and tetrahedron (which points to the runway in use) for myself; many small airports have no radio to advise you and it is mighty important to find the sock or tetrahedron in order to learn which way the wind is blowing and which runway is in use.

In my elation at having found our way to a large, well-marked airport over one of the easiest possible routes to follow, I performed a somewhat less than smooth landing. Bumpy, but safe. All that was damaged was my piloting pride. Tom smiled knowingly again and I looked over at him, irritated at the way he could read my thoughts. After all, he'd only gone through this a few hundred times before.

Joanne checked the watch and worked with her mysterious pencil as we taxied in; we had covered the 52 miles in 28 minutes: 118 mph. To us, the flight seemed not only to have taken much more time, but we felt we'd covered a vastly greater distance.

We were pleased, satisfied and wary; we'd passed a small hurdle. But we had at the same time learned a new respect for the old-time fliers who followed the "iron compass"—the railroads across the country—in all kinds of ugly weather without any navigational aids. We had gained immense respect for the men who had once crossed oceans guided only by a simple compass—and their own faith in themselves, the most important asset a flier can have. We now knew the beginnings of that faith, one which was to steadily grow with our skill as the two of us sought the sky.

Chapter Ten. WEATHER OR NOT

"The air moves like a river and carries the clouds with it."
LEONARDO DA VINCI

Many of us have flown enough in bad weather and have read enough about instrument flying to have a healthy respect for all the kinds of weather that fill our skies over America. Somehow, most people before taking up flying never think of weather in deeply personal terms. They never think that an air mass moving over the earth can touch them so strongly, or as quickly, as it does when you're in the sky.

One lesson had been brought home to us early in our flying. Cruising above the Hudson River, returning from a cross-country flight, we were flying level at 3000 feet. Just above us, a thin but solid layer of flat gray clouds had gradually drifted in from the southwest. Without even thinking about it, we began dropping the plane down to 2000 feet to separate ourselves from the clouds by a comfortable margin.

Then, without warning, great pinging noises beat on the windshield and the wings, as if machine guns loaded with BBs had been trained on the plane. For a few minutes, it rained furiously and forward visibility all but disappeared. Helpless, we beat our way back toward Ramapo Valley, with the trusty Lycoming's bass crescendo muted by the pinging of the rain.

There was no real danger; the rain ended almost as abruptly as it had begun and the sky opened up again in front of us. The propwash quickly dried the windshield. The shower was over. But we had learned another lesson, for we had not expected any rain. Then and there, we resolved to learn a lot more in a hurry about weather and to listen more closely when flight weather or an FAA Flight Service Station warned of a "chance of isolated showers."

More than five hundred United States Weather Bureau airport weather stations span the country; hundreds of FAA towers and many hundreds of VOR and VORTAC stations also provide fast, complete and generally accurate weather information for the pilot. Some 150 of the Weather Bureau stations send up balloons at six-hour intervals to report on wind speed and directions in the stratosphere, a valuable hint as to what will develop down below. Scores of radiosonde devices

Cumulus dead ahead. We go under or around, but not through. This stuff is just bouncy – for now. A warm day full of this type of cloud can end in the nasty kind of cumulonimbus: thunderstorms.

—transmitters in balloons—are sent up at twelve-hour intervals to report on humidity, atmospheric pressure and temperature.

Four times daily, at six-hour intervals, all the flight advisory weather centers send out forecasts on flying conditions expected over the next twelve hours over the twenty-four areas the United States is divided into for flight weather. These are called "area" forecasts. At the same time, following the *six-hour pattern,* "*terminal*" forecasts are sent out for nearly four hundred of the United States' major airports.

The weather is further covered in "sequence" reports, which are filed hourly by the principal FAA stations. These cover full conditions on the hour at the given station. All of these forecasting aids are on tap at airports, weather bureaus, and on the FAA's very high frequency (VHF) and low frequency (LF) broadcasts, at fifteen minutes past and fifteen minutes before each hour. Any pilot can get them on the ground by phone, or in the air by radio with a call to the nearest FAA range station or tower.

Before taking off on a trip, a pilot puts in a call to the nearest FAA station or airport weather bureau, and gets himself briefed on what to expect. He simply tells them he is a pilot, declares what route he expects to follow, when he expects to leave (ETD) and arrive (ETA) and whether he'll be flying strictly according to VFR (Visual Flight Rules) or IFR (Instrument Flight Rules). The man on duty will then lay out his latest reports and tell you what conditions are being reported on your route, and what the weather is likely to be when you fly past given stations. Yet, with all of these aids, too many private pilots (as we'll see) still ignore the helping hand and take off blindly into dangerous weather conditions. The result too often is tragic.

A new FAA program to make general aviation safer is now in progress—the VFR Flight Following Service. Upwards of four hundred of FAA's Flight Service Stations (FSS) around the country will furnish this service—which is like a friend following you all the way in flight telling you what is happening on your route to any pilot filing a VFR flight plan and requesting service.

You are passed on from station to station, and they'll call you on the standard frequency in your plane. Some of the more valuable information given: the current flight advisories; severe weather warnings; PIREPS or pilot reports on unusual conditions; flight conditions along your route; the forecasts; and even NOTAMS, Notices to Airmen, that affect the radio ranges, airports or other services you may need. The new service is the biggest step forward for private flying FAA has ever taken.

Using these services, and with a basic general knowledge of what weather is, any pilot is safe flying anywhere in the United States—if he listens to his good sense. But some study of weather, winds and clouds is necessary.

Meteorologists used to think that the heating of the earth from the sun was the cause of most of our abnormal weather conditions—storms, fronts and the like. Our headlong rush into the Space Age has already produced preliminary data indicating the reason is more complex. Sunstorms producing solar radiation, the electrical charges in the atmosphere, and even the currents in the ocean may all combine to produce the woes and wonders of our earth weather.

We know that changes in atmospheric pressure and in temperature results in motion in the air, causing upward and downward currents and horizontal movement—the wind itself. The heat of the sun, which is greater at the equator than anywhere else on earth, warms the air, expands it and causes it to rise. This produces low pressure areas at the equator; the cooler air from the polar regions moves in on this air, absorbing some of its heat and balancing the low pressure with highs from the polar regions. The end result is a flow of air that weathermen think works along two elliptical paths: shooting upward from the equator, then branching outward toward the North and South Poles and returning along the surface to the equator.

But it is not quite that simple. The air flow is controlled and changed by the oceans, the land masses, the rotation of the Earth, and by low pressure zones created by highly heated land areas.

The high and low pressure areas that result from the complex mixing of all these weather patterns produces much of the weather pilots have to worry about. From these highs and lows, a discernible pattern of winds emerges.

When examined in simplified form, these winds nearly always flow from west to east over the United States. The wind is pushed to the right of its course, principally by the rotation of the Earth and the effect of the jet streams. Thus, flying from New York to Los Angeles you nearly always can expect a head wind; going the opposite route you'll nearly always pick up speed from a tail wind. But even this is modified by the specific high or low prevailing. The air pouring out of a high pressure mass flows clockwise; from a low pressure mass it flows counterclockwise. The result is that a really crack pilot going from New York to Los Angeles again will fly south of a high and pick up a good wind, or if a low prevails, go to the north of it to get another good wind.

This could be called the big picture of the winds. All too often, it means very little for your little picture—flying in or around your local airport. In such a narrow area, terrain, heat and other factors help produce wind variations and smooth or bumpy air. The air may be cool and calm at 10,000 feet. But down at 2000 it may be turbulent and uncomfortably bumpy. On a hot day, the wind will pour off a high ridge, forcing your plane upward as it approaches the windward side of the ridge, and dragging it down on the opposite or lee side.

Empty farm fields, sandy beaches or other types of good reflecting surfaces tend to pour the sun's heat up at your plane, bouncing it around. But if you happen to be going over water, the air will be smooth; and flying over forests or active farms, the air will be much calmer than over the "bouncy" types of terrain. What results from all this heating is called convection motion.

Currents of convection rise off the Earth and produce dramatic differences in the way your plane will fly and land. For example, if you happen to be trying to land on a hot day on an approach over empty fields, the updrafts will push you beyond your touchdown spot unless you take them into account. On the other hand, if you are approaching over water, the convection current will drag you down a bit; and in a pure glide without power, you could easily land short unless you take action in time and add power.

Another valuable weather clue can be read right off any weather map, the kind published in most newspapers. The little items that look like musical notes indicate the velocity of wind, and the direction that they point in graphically illustrates the direction of the surface wind. And on this same map unevenly shaped circles, consecutively drawn around the center of the high or low, give you a good idea of the area and character of the weather. In weathermen's lingo these circles are called isobars (a good crossword puzzle word).

They accurately tell the difference in barometric pressure over different regions. Tracking them in order will produce the exact center of lows or highs. There's no real need to get that precise about the job of preflight with weather. But isobars furnish a good tip on winds aloft, if you want to take time to study them. Generally speaking, wind will move parallel to isobars at a speed greater than that indicated on the maps. So while the wind arrows on the weather map tell you what to expect on the surface, the isobars themselves can give you clues about the winds at flight altitude.

An old rule of pilots about wind is this: figure it at roughly 45° to the right of the way it is blowing on the surface when you're flying along at 2000 feet. Roughly again, the wind will, at that altitude, be about double the speed of the surface readings.

Carried inside this huge mass of moving air, the wind has a great deal of moisture, a kind of invisible water vapor. The amount of vapor the air can contain is determined by its temperature. For every 20° Fahrenheit increase in temperature the air doubles its humidity capacity. Every time the temperature drops 20°, the capacity of the air to hold water cuts itself in half. Humidity is the familiar word with which we describe moisture in the air. Pilots define moisture conditions in terms of dew point. For example, if you knew that the temperature was 70° and the humidity 50 per cent, a drop of 20° would result in so much moisture that—voilà! rain. But, to the pilot on reading a weather map, or receiving information from an FAA weather station, it would be stated as temperature 70°, dew point 50. No mathematics are necessary to know that when the temperature of the air then drops to 50°, dew point condensation will be along in the form of fog, clouds, or falling to earth as rain, snow, sleet or hail.

This first form of fog or clouds that may develop when dew point and temperature shake hands are of two basic types. *Cumulus* (meaning accumulation or a pile) are the result of vertical currents carrying moist air upward to cooler areas and condensing. Cumulus are lumpy or billowy in appearance. *Stratus* (meaning spread out) clouds develop horizontally and lie in layers like a gray fog when close to the ground.

It only takes a small basic vocabulary to accurately describe cloud formations. It largely combines basic descriptive words with the roots of *cumulus* and *stratus*.

If there is rain, *nimbo* (meaning rain) is added—*nimbostratus* or *cumulonimbus.*

Fracto (meaning broken) yields a combination of *fractostratus* or *fractocumulus* totaling up to broken or ragged formations.

For moderately high clouds, 5000 to 20,000 feet, the word *alto* (meaning high) is the key—*altostratus* or *altocumulus.*

And for the upper-level clouds, 20,000 to 50,000 feet, which are made up of ice crystals and have a delicate, curly appearance, *cirro* is the descriptive word that forms into *cirrocumulus* or *cirrostratus.*

Also found at this high altitude are the colorfully described "mare's tail" or *cirrus* clouds.

Small planes never fly at these high altitudes, but it's important to recognize these clouds as visual indicators of types of weather. Even the *alto-* group, which again small planes seldom reach, serve to predict icing conditions (beware!) and the approach of bad flying weather.

Now let's consider those formations to watch and beware of on the weather map, the kinds of clouds that all too often mean low ceilings and low visibility. Their quixotic ability to shift and lower, and to cause icing, must be recognized and reacted to. Head for the nearest safe landing or make the wise 180° turn where possible. The time for action can arise out of scattered cumulus gathering in the late part of the day and sloping into a flattened-out front with the possibility of high winds, squalls and rain.

Act! Don't wait and spend too much time looking for a way around these clouds. There is always a welcome cup of coffee at the nearest airport and other weathered-in birdmen to talk flying with.

With *cumulonimbus,* whether there is just one or a frontal thunderstorm, makes no difference. Remember that cumulonimbus clouds are formed by rising air currents and quickly become very turbulent. If you're flying in the vicinity of a real thunderstorm, you can be sucked into a condition of winds up to 150 mph that would make quick work of any small plane. And if your plane wasn't ripped apart, it could very well be pelleted apart by hailstones in the thunderhead.

CIRRUS – The long stretched-out streamers are a sure clue to pin down the strong, shearing winds of the jet stream. Cirrus, when it moves in from the northwest, generally means continued fine weather. When it spreads from the southwest, beware of rain.

ALTOCUMULUS – The rolling motion of these clouds can tell you the direction of the winds aloft. The wind blows across the corrugations at right angles to the rolling motion. Flying conditions near these clouds: light to moderate turbulence.

STRATOCUMULUS – Above these flat cloud decks, it'll be smooth flying. But the top surface is the sign of an inversion where temperature will increase with altitude. Descending through the deck in wintertime, watch out for icing.

CUMULONIMBUS – The deadly thunderstorm clouds are commonly known as "CB." When such storms begin to line up in the northeast to southwest during the late afternoon be wary of a squall line developing. The danger of squalls will generally decrease by late night.

Beware! Beware! warn wise pilots, of the anvil-shaped cloud, with the anvil pointing in the direction the cloud is moving. The prevailing wind will be on top, pulling you in near the base; the violent updrafts at the forward, lower edge; the strong downdraft in the rear, blowing away from the cloud. If you are foolhardy enough to get caught, throttle back to twice stalling speed (90–100 mph in most small planes), and never exceed your cruising speed. Thus, you'll reduce the strain on the structure of the plane.

Another good thing to remember is that it is impossible for the small plane to go above these airborne engines of destruction. They sometimes reach altitudes of 50,000 feet. It also is difficult, if not impossible, to scoot under them—they often nearly touch the ground. And to go around them, unless you can give them an extremely wide berth, is useless, because they move so fast and extend their tentacles for so many miles that you may be trapped. Go down! Land! We guarantee it will be no forty-day Noah-like deluge. They generally are gone within a few hours.

Up to now, we've been talking about how high or low clouds are. Now let's use the correct term, ceiling. If there are no clouds, or more than half the sky visible from your front door is free of clouds, you are generally blessed with an "unlimited" ceiling. When you obtain the latest information on ceilings from the

The T-storm, enemy of pilots and airplanes, can take several different forms, depending on the stage of its developments. The hammerhead and anvil shapes exhibited in T-storms mark a line of severe turbulence and storm activity. With a T-storm, play it safe: when in doubt go by another route. . . .

hourly sequence reports, the information available at weather stations, these reports give you the measured ceiling from the lowest layer of clouds that cover more than half the sky to the ground.

The distance you can see across the horizon from that same front door is called visibility. On a weather map this information is reported in miles or fractions of miles. If it exceeds ten miles, it's unlimited on the weather map, though a weather station will express it in longer distances.

The ceiling may be unlimited, the visibility better than ten miles, but you are still grounded until every bit of snow is removed from your plane and until you've chipped off that last crust of ice on your tail section and wings. And always check your controls before taking off after a freezing rain. They have a nasty habit of sometimes icing up and it doesn't get any warmer to clear them when you're aloft.

This huge ocean of air we live in is not a static thing. There is a constant movement of air masses. These masses originate in one of five areas, and a look at the weather map will not only tell where they originate, but give a positive identification of their characteristics, even though they have been constantly changing as they pass over land and sea surfaces.

The following symbols on the map indicate the source of air masses:

A – arctic
P – polar
T – tropical
M – maritime (formed over oceans)
C – continental (formed over land)

From this you can see that an air mass originating in the polar region will be colder (noted by K) than the areas it is passing over; an air mass originating in the tropics will be warmer (noted by W) than the northerly area it's traveling over. This cold air mass passing over warmer parts, by the way, would be represented by the symbol cPK (for continental air mass originating in polar region that is cold). However, by the time this mass passes over Mount Washington in New Hampshire, it might have warmed and the symbol would then be cPW.

Since the air masses can be either warm or cold, let's break down these two categories to get a more accurate picture:

	Cold Air Mass	Warm Air Mass
Cloud types	Cumulus and cumulonimbus	Stratus and stratocumulus (fog and haze)
Ceiling	Generally unlimited, unless there is precipitation	Generally low
Visibility	Very good, again unless there is precipitation	Poor—smoke and dust held in lower layers
Precipitation	Some local thunderstorms or showers with hail, sleet, snow flurries	Drizzle
Air stability	Decided turbulence in lower levels—result of convection currents	Smooth with little or no turbulence

The constant movement of the air mass is not without a pattern. As was noted earlier, the basic motion across the United States is to the east. Movement toward the northeast is dominated by tropical and equatorial air; polar and arctic air masses usually move toward the southeast. The bodies of air will move somewhere around 500 to 700 miles a day, with cold air masses traveling faster than warm air masses.

What happens when two or more of these air masses meet? Unless they are very similar in temperature, pressure and relative humidity, there is an exchange of forces not too unlike the children's game of King of the Mountain. They exert a force on each other, with one displacing the other, wearing the other out; or wearing each other out when, in some instances, each firmly holds its ground.

The rule of King of the Mountain in weather terms is called frontal zones or "fronts." If two fronts exist that are holding their ground with little movement and with the cold air mass wedged under the warm, it is called a "stationary front." It bears careful watching.

But now what happens when the warm front tries to gain ascendancy? The warm air mass goes about its business of displacing the cold air mass by going *over* the wedge of colder air and gaining its throne. The result as far as flying weather is concerned is a gradual sloping of the front that may climb a mile vertically, within a horizontal area of from 100 to 500 miles. It averages about 150 miles.

In this area, you will find high humidity and lowering of temperature caused by the warm and cold fronts meeting. Drizzle and rain result as dew point and temperature meet.

Now, as the front climbs higher and the temperature falls, the clouds, because of the moisture-laden air, become *altostratus* and *cirrostratus*. Finally, as it reaches the stratosphere with its freezing temperatures, all that remains are thin wispy cirrus clouds.

Warm fronts move at a speed from 10 to 25 miles per hour. The activity of a warm front can be easily recognized. Look for a falling barometer (warm air has less weight than the cold air it is replacing). The cloud formation, if you approach from the warm air side (though two are never alike), has a very recognizable pattern: *cirrus* followed by *cirrostratus* and finally the denser clouds of the front itself. That halo you see around a summer moon from high-altitude moisture is a good indicator of unstable warm air. If the halo gets larger, the front is departing (the warm air is rising higher). If you're approaching the front, the halo decreases. On the other hand, if you approach from the cold air side, look out for *altostratus* and *altocumulus* clouds that continue to get lower and lower as well as thicker with precipitation and occasional hidden thunderheads.

The hazards in flying through a warm front are minor to an experienced instrument pilot. But it does mean, because of the extended low ceilings encountered, long periods of total reliance on your plane's instruments. And never to be forgotten are those hidden thunderheads and the danger of icing.

Let's return to our two fronts. The cold front has burrowed its way under the warm air mass and gained supremacy. It goes about tossing the warm front out of its kingdom with quite a bit more gusto. No time is wasted and the front moves through from 30 to 35 mph. This volatile weather condition, with sudden storms, high winds and turbulence, can be dangerous to the flyer. And it seldom bothers to give a formal announcement.

It develops in the space of a few hours. The belt of storm activity, called the "squall line," may only be 50 to 100 miles wide, but it can also extend across the United States in a line running from northeast to southwest. The only warning you get of thunderheads, turbulent weather and icing conditions accompanying the cold front are the *altostratus* clouds that sometimes form slightly ahead of it. The overcast sky with *stratocumulus* clouds is to be regarded like a bill collector. Don't be fooled by it's relatively calm air and try to cheat ceilings and visibilities that are low but still within minimums for VFR flying. Be patient. It, too, will pass and leave in its wake unlimited ceilings and visibilities—the pilot's dream of good flying weather.

No description of fronts can be complete without explaining wind shifts. Whenever you fly out of one front into another, or fly through the point where the fronts overtake one another (the frontal line), here is what takes place: the wind shifts from left to right relative to you no matter what the kind of front.

Now say an interloper—a crazy, misguided air mass—finds its way into our King of the Mountain tussle. It gets itself caught or blocked between two colder fronts. It is called an occluded front, because it is blocked between them. What happens is that the two cold fronts then proceed to push it in until it is just dissipated into the upper atmosphere.

The weather found in an occlusion is a warm- and cold-front combination. At the beginning of the occlusion, warm-front conditions prevail: lowered ceilings and visibility and precipitation. This is followed quickly by the cold front with thunderstorms, rain squalls and severe turbulence.

An interesting note about weather is that the forecasters never get tired of giving you information—never get tired of taking the time to explain to a pilot what to expect. In fact, they respect the pilot who wants to know the full story, rather than the character who demands a few quick facts and dashes off without being fully prepared. Weather conditions change so rapidly that it pays to make that extra call while refueling, to check or to examine the sequence reports again even though you went over them only an hour or two ago. That's the purpose of the sequences—they're the latest hourly teletype data sent out by weather stations. The time used learning the symbols is well spent: it'll save you delays and unplanned landings at a later date.

Chapter Eleven. CROSS-COUNTRY

THE LOGBOOK OF ONE ZERO ZULU—
"SHOW ME THE WAY TO GO HOME"

Sooner or later, every pilot has to go off on a cross-country flight on his own, and this is where you must start using your own newly acquired judgment on weather, as well as navigation.

The issue can be evaded for a while, but never avoided. There comes the day when you have to get somewhere at a given time, and the weather will be neither black nor white. The choice you'll have to make won't be automatic, with a 300-foot ceiling simply scrubbing the mission. It'll be gray, with marginal ceilings of 1500 feet and visibility hovering around three miles—near the legal minimums.

The sooner, the better. The sooner it happens, all the more quickly you begin to build your ability to use critical judgment. Conditions will probably change while you're in the air; this will be even better for testing your ability to judge. Nearly perfect, clear days can deteriorate into marginal and unacceptable VFR conditions very rapidly, especially in the East. The pilot who keeps right on going into the jaws of black clouds is in just as bad trouble as the fool who takes off blindly into them. And the fact that you had the sense not to take off into bad weather, but lacked the judgment to land when the weather got too sticky, makes you equally guilty and sorry.

All too frequently, you'll take off and get through in less than perfect—but acceptable—weather, learning to watch it closely as you go along. This is the prime purpose for the cross-country flight time you need to build up before you can get your license.

We had been rained out four weekends in a row; a succession of late spring thunderstorms had cleared the air of planes, as well as of New York's dust, in a hurry. Joanne had already flown her long cross-country hop (by FAA regulations, two flights of more than a hundred miles each way, landing at a distant airport) and this, coupled with her demonstrated superiority at landings, had left my male confidence shattered, with my pride crawling into a dark chasm. Secretly, she rejoiced at a rainy weekend; it gave us a chance to catch up with

Nothing is better than a smokestack for telling you what the wind is doing to your airplane . . .

chores around the house. She could afford to rejoice; her cross-country had come off on the scheduled day with no problems whatsoever.

But I kept getting "weathered out." And, with the natural uncertainty and worry about the first long flight alone, it began to work on me full-time. Despite my experience navigating sailboats and in hiking, I had a deep and wholly unsuppressed fear of getting lost somewhere in the clouds as the sun was setting and bad weather rolling in. However, I had good company; there's hardly a flier alive who isn't willing to confess to the same fear.

Just listen to any of them, especially on rainy or threatening afternoons when they congregate at the airport checking the weather every hour or so, and exchanging stories all the time. The old-timers keep a wary eye on the newcomers, particularly those who have just gotten their private license. They are full of confidence and impatient to go somewhere, anywhere just to get in the air, and often just a little too cocky.

The scant fifty or more hours between getting his private license and before he gets to one hundred hours of experience and really acquires skill and caution is rated as the most dangerous time period in a new pilot's life. As a student with thirty hours in my logbook at that point I was worried that I was too cautious, using the bad weather as an excuse to put off the cross-country trip. I kept telling myself that this was playing it safe, and so did the pros—the trouble was, I wasn't sure.

Deep inside you know when you're ready to go; and right to your face, the instructor will tell you when you're ready.

Some people have to be told, and gently prodded; they'll keep putting off the flight until it becomes a monster entirely out of proportion. On the other hand, most students are in a hurry to get out and go. You can't go until the instructor signs your logbook, saying you can go; he wants to be sure, too.

There's only one way ultimately to overcome your fear, and that is to go, to prove to yourself that with maps, compass, radio and what you have learned, that you can find your way.

The bad weather, I knew deep inside, had been a convenient—though eminently sensible and correct—excuse not to go; another excuse was a persistently pesky magneto on the plane's ignition, which ran roughly at annoying times (when I was ready to take off, or just short of the field).

The big difference in handling excuses and rationalizations when flying—as opposed to being on the ground—is that you use the excuse—and do the safe thing—until you're reasonably sure nothing is wrong. This sometimes takes a little pushing, because no one likes to let go of a convenient rationalization; but never fear, there's always an instructor around who never heard of such things as rationalizations or the subconscious; he'll give you the extra needed push.

Saturday dawned crystal-clear and cool. A front had blown through the day before, clearing out the smoke and haze from the city and its factories. Another front was due through that night, but it left at least eight perfect flying hours in between—or so the weatherman promised.

I had charted my course—from Teterboro to Trumbull Field, New London, Connecticut—the night before. It was an area I hadn't flown to before, which made it an interesting trip, and I wanted to look at a sailboat for sale near New London. Coming back, I figured on cutting north into Connecticut to make the flight back along a different route.

There could be few problems, and yet nervous anticipation had produced a ragged night's sleep and I awoke early, anxious to get started. Not only was Tom there, in spirit anyway, urging me on, but Joanne had a thermos of coffee and a sandwich waiting even before I sat down to breakfast and made up my mind about going. She'd checked the weather while I was still sleeping.

By the time I arrived at Teterboro, the perfect blue of the sky was splotched by broken bits of cumulus clouds—not enough to be a problem, but an indication of the warming trend and the front. And also, since they were at 5000 feet, they would produce updrafts and downdrafts with enough turbulence to make the flight a bouncy if not downright uncomfortable affair.

Newark Airport's flight weather station predicted generally good weather all the way to and from New London, except for a prediction of scattered thundershowers back at Teterboro at just about the time I would be landing.

Consultations were clearly in order, and my quiet queries to several instructors produced a general consensus of: get in the air, see how it looks, and then call the aviation weather station at the Wilton, Connecticut, omni-range radio station. Tune in on Wilton omni (or Teterboro omni) and cross-check my course as I flew. I could also call Wilton on 122.1, the standard frequency for checking FAA radio and flight advisory service, and ask them how the weather was developing.

It was a soggy 85° on the runway as I ground-checked the Tri-Pacer, got her fueled, and hurriedly laid out my maps, radio chart, and plotter in the front seat. There were only three other planes warming up, waiting for clearance (everyone at Teterboro was cooperating, since there usually were ten planes waiting), and I was soon roaring down runway 24.

Halfway, just as I lifted the nose wheel off, I remembered with a sting of pain and annoyance that I had forgotten to compute my drift angle and to figure a course based on the wind's effect on the plane. I kicked myself mentally, but it was no great problem, since visibility was a marvelous (for New York) seven to eight miles, and I would at first be hugging the shore line of Long Island Sound. Keeping the plane over the shore would automatically correct my drift, and a look at the compass course required to keep me on my track would tell me quickly enough what the wind was doing. (It was out of the west-northwest at 15 mph, thus giving me a nice tailwind with a slightly quartering effect, pushing me a bit to the southeast.)

Clearing Teterboro's pattern, in a climbing 45° turn at 600 feet, I did a climbing turn to 3500 feet—my cruising altitude to New London—and came to my course heading. My fears dissipated in the busy rhythm of setting up the course, and I found I'd at least remembered the basic rule of altitude for traffic control over 3000 feet; flying from 0° to 179°, you pick an odd altitude, plus 500 feet; from 180° to 359°, an even altitude plus 500 feet. Going up on a heading of 77° to New Haven, I would be at 3500 feet. Coming back on a heading of 277°, I'd cruise at 2500 feet just below the control altitude—or that was what I thought.

I crossed the Hudson River just above the George Washington Bridge, lined up on course and tuned in Wilton omni after cranking the very high frequency radio to 113.6 megacycles. This should be as easy as it sounds, but the air was plenty turbulent, and it was difficult to keep the plane flying straight and level, let alone crank up two radios and set up a gyro compass. I felt I should be an octopus; I needed more hands than I had in order to do everything. Trying to find Wilton by pinning down its weak Morse code signal wasn't easy either; the omni stations are only one-tenth of a megacycle apart; Wilton was 113.6; another station, theoretically out of range, but often loud and clear, would be at 113.8. Bouncing around in turbulent air, they can all sound alike and it takes careful code identification to pick up the right one. As I crossed Yonkers, my first checkpoint (an even ten miles from Teterboro), I got Wilton weakly and checked out the weather.

"Tri-Pacer 10 Zulu," he answered promptly, "this is Wilton Radio." As he launched into the terminal and area forecasts, his voice disappeared in a jumble of static and interception. It sounded like a demonstration lesson in radio jamming

The George Washington Bridge and New York City through the struts.

technique. The reception was so bad that the poor man had to repeat the forecasts for Poughkeepsie, Bridgeport, Providence and New York three times before I was able to get the entire prediction and grasp the best part: a new forecast eliminated the possibility of thundershowers. Or rather, it removed any mention of them; no one has ever removed the possibility of sudden thundershowers in summer flying.

By this time, I was passing Greenwich, my third or thirty-mile checkpoint. (Rye, my second checkpoint, had been neglected while I was trying to get the forecast.) Long Island Sound sparkled below, crammed with thousands of sailboats scurrying in all directions. But every time I took my eyes off the instruments and the horizon to sneak a look, I'd find the plane off course, or climbing or descending—being buffeted by the wind and up- and downdrafts in the turbulent air. There was a beautiful sea running, a bright blue sky, and regattas I'd have loved to follow, but I had no time for sightseeing or relaxation in that air.

With the omni still cranked into Wilton, I could follow my on-course progress. Over Norwalk, which is on a 180° radial from Wilton, I watched the needle center at 180, just when and where it was supposed to.

Bridgeport was my halfway mark, and as I passed just east of the airport I tried calling the tower to check the weather again. The Tri-Pacer's radio didn't have the right frequency—120.9—for transmitting to Bridgeport, so I called on 122.5, a standard tower frequency all over the world, and still got no answer. It didn't occur to me until Tom chided me later for trying to receive them on 122.5—not the published 120.9 (which my receiver did have), that they'd undoubtedly been answering me and I'd never heard them because I was tuned to the wrong frequency. Tower men can tell a student from an experienced commercial pilot in just a few words; they'd found a live one that day, all right.

I changed course over New Haven and, with visibility actually improving, I was able to spot Trumbull before crossing the Connecticut River at Old Saybrook. I entered the pattern at Trumbull with a sweeping turn over the Sound and made a satisfactory if not too smooth landing while bucking a crosswind off the Sound.

Trumbull Field had Unicom (the airman's universal radio communications channel) and I followed their advice on the selection of a runway, even though it looked—as I scanned the field before going in—more as if the other runway should have been in use. You can't be sure; the wind might have just swung around a few moments before, and they might not have noticed the change, or a gust may have changed the sock just for the few seconds I'd looked.

Trumbull is a state-owned field without a federal weather station, and when

CROSS-COUNTRY

Lakes can be great landmarks, as long as there aren't too many of them looking too much alike in too small an area.

Hartford under the wing.

Another friendly turnpike below.

Princeton, New Jersey, Airport. The grass strips *look* smooth; just wait until your wheels clunk into the potholes.

The Iron Compass, which is what the old airmail pilots flew by when their somewhat-less-than-reliable compasses erred, or the weather was so bad they had to fly just over the boxcars.

I asked what the latest forecast was, I ended up by telling *them*. An unshaven gray-haired crew-cut type in a battered leather jacket ambled over from his sleek twin-engined Beech Travel-Air to introduce himself and ask if I'd picked up the forecast for Nantucket. He was going over to visit his family for the weekend. As I gave him the forecast, I thought to myself, Ah, here's one of the old-time stick-and-rudder men exactly as Hollywood would cast him. Then he started talking; it turned out that he was a film producer who made documentaries about flying. He treated me with such respect as I professionally recited the ceiling, visibility and general weather conditions, that I was downright ashamed to tell him how many hours I had in my logbook when he asked.

I was too leery of the clouds to take any time out for a look at the boat and, after a sandwich, took off right after his Travel-Air, still feeling nothing but a beaming confidence in myself and the weather.

On a hunch, I followed the shore line back for a while, retracing my steps, instead of turning inland. At 2500 feet, the turbulence was now even worse, and I looked longingly at the broken clouds overhead, which were now both a lot less broken and a lot lower. They were no longer at 5000 feet but closer to 3000. Remembering the FAA rule about not climbing over clouds that were getting *solid* without an instrument rating and instrument flight rules (IFR) clearance, and Tom's advice about taking the bumps, but not getting trapped over the clouds, I kept right on going at 2500 feet.

To the west, the playful, puffy cumulus had suddenly grown into something much more businesslike—towering *cumulonimbus* stretching up to 40,000 feet, which often build into full-grown thunderstorms. It was beautiful white cottony stuff at least 60 miles wide, stretching almost from the Sound far north into Connecticut. I was at one edge and somewhere north I imagined another flier was probably at the other extremity, getting jittery just like me.

Clouds, made up of moisture vapor in the atmosphere, are masterful actors; just in the few seconds I glanced at it, this one changed roles from a soft-spoken, reasonable fellow to a no-back-talk maniac ready to maul anybody who crossed his path. A master makeup man worked with the cloud, changing its attractive white in a split second to a menacing gray-black, and then to a purple blue-black. In weatherman's lingo, the cloud was passing from its cumulus or buildup stage to its mature or get-out-of-the-way-pronto stage. As I sat watching, wondering what the storm was going to do, it *did* it, building with frightening speed into a full front.

All my life I've photographed clouds, mystified and drawn to them by some poetic beauty they hold. This one was no different, but now I knew suddenly what it meant to me at this moment: danger. In the sky, storm clouds are treacherous enemies of aircraft, packing high velocity up- and downdrafts, fierce rain, hail and ice—enough to cripple the biggest planes flying, let alone a fragile small plane. My confidence drained away with the sweat that suddenly began coming down my forehead. I was now beyond Bridgeport, a bit more than half-way home, and I had no intention of turning back and landing at Bridgeport unless it was absolutely imperative for safety's sake.

My faithful friend answering at Wilton omni—really a man at Idlewild talking through Wilton—was still on duty, but with the storm over his transmitter I could hardly hear him through the static. The forecast he gave me was still for fair weather, some broken clouds, and no sign of thunderfronts.

Somewhat indignantly, I advised him to take a look out of his window, and sarcastically added that these nonexistent storms were overhead. He thanked me profusely and said good-bye. I'd filed my first PIREP—pilot's report—a running road report on the weather, which pilot passes on to pilot, warning each other what to expect. The PIREP is the flier's best friend and his most accurate source of weather information.

But even in the few moments I'd been on the radio, the storm had finished building to a full front. Ugly gray-black striated lines reached down into the green Connecticut countryside, lacing it with rain and battering it with high winds. The winds inside thunderstorms have been clocked at 150 mph. The storm, though malevolent, was still beautiful, a brilliant color spectacle. If there had been a castle nearby on a high mountain, I could have photographed it and had a reasonable twentieth-century version of El Greco's "View of Toledo." The rain was a good ten miles away, but the front was spreading out rapidly and I found myself edging farther and farther out over the Sound, avoiding the storm as if it were someone at a party with a bad cold.

Flying over water at low altitude in a single-engine aircraft isn't the best of ideas, but I had no other choice, and I was still close enough in to make land. To the south and west, the skies were still open, though visibility had dropped, and I knew I could make a run for it—to LaGuardia Airport on Long Island, or Newark Airport in New Jersey—if I had to. I could still go faster than the storm.

As the front pushed out, its downward force spilled out high winds, curving upward like a howitzer shell, and since I was on the edge, the shell kept boring into the Tri-Pacer. I was riding a roller coaster. The moderately turbulent air was really jumping now. The plane soared upward on fantastic updrafts produced by the edge of the storm, and in a few seconds I was over 5000 feet; my rate-of-climb indicator read 700 feet a minute while I was at cruising power with the nose held down. The Tri-Pacer, for all purposes, was a sailplane. As soon as the updraft would give out, we'd go scooting downward, back to 2500 feet. When I mentally pictured what the airplane's path of flight must have looked like from the side, my stomach began to knot up even more.

Bobbing around in the air like a cork on storm-tossed seas, I could hardly keep track of my altitude and the attitude of the plane, let alone try to keep on course. Each time I looked the storm seemed to have pulled closer to One Zero Zulu, and I felt more alone and helpless than I ever have in my life. I focused hard on the gyro compass, which I was trying to keep at 265°—my trail back—and mumbled in a low voice, "Show me the way to go home, baby."

Suddenly, reassuringly, I had company on both wing tips—an Eastern Airlines Electra just inboard of me, also skirting the storm's border, and an American Convair, scooting by on my left wing tip, their navigation lights blinking a tri-colored red-green-white warning in the darkening air. Mine had been on for ten minutes in the darkened sky.

I was now south of Westchester, and the towers of the George Washington Bridge loomed up dimly ahead, welcoming sentinels in a suddenly unfriendly land. I changed course to make a beeline for the bridge and save a few moments.

I'd grown up near the bridge and had helped pay for it with countless tolls. Now, crossing over it free of charge, I felt I was getting an extra free bonus. But the Port of New York Authority could have charged whatever toll they wanted at that moment and I would have thought it most reasonable.

Over the Hudson River again, I switched over to Teterboro's frequency and called in. The familiar nasal twang of a tower controller from Brooklyn (an anonymous voice I've heard hundreds of times) called back faithfully: "Tri-Pacer One Zero Zulu . . . Teterboro tower . . . runway 32 for full stop . . . 24 for touch and go . . . wind west-northwest 12 miles an hour . . . altimeter . . . 29.92 . . . report on downwind."

The wind was still out of the west-northwest. I glanced at my computer; I'd only made 95 mph battling the head wind back to Teterboro. Going out with that brisk tail wind, I'd made nearly 120 mph. It was that tricky old wind again, the invisible current of the sky, constantly moving, silent and emotionless, around the earth, yet dictating whether thousands of planes would reach their destination on time (and whether some, whose pilots had been too careless, would reach it at all).

Runway 32 was for full-stop landings; students were still shooting touch-and-go landings on runway 24. I'd never before landed on 32 and mentally plotted out my downwind approach and began my descent. I turned downwind at 900 feet, still a trifle high, and called in then, and again as I turned base leg. Turning for my final approach I was still at 700 feet, and a good thing it was, too, because just as I lined up the Tri-Pacer for the runway, a Cessna 140 shot in under me not 100 feet away, blindly breaking right into the pattern.

The tower excitedly asked me to make a 360° turn to the right and come in on final again. I was shaking so hard I could do nothing but half stutter, half mumble, "One . . . One . . . Zero . . . Zulu . . . Roger." The Tri-Pacer had dropped to 400 feet in those few seconds, and I used full power, shoving the throttle to the fire wall in a climbing 360° turn, coming out at 1000 feet lined up with runway 32 again. Or was it 1000 feet? I looked again and my eyes were suddenly bleary; the altimeter seemed to say 1800 feet, then 1700 feet. I was only half a mile from the runway threshold and I knew I could never lose enough altitude in that short a distance to land. Without thinking, I automatically pulled full back on the throttle, killing all the power; I trimmed the nose down and came back on the wheel, slowing the Tri-Pacer down, and quickly put down full flap, to shorten my glide path as much as possible and lose as much altitude as rapidly as I could. Still too far out, I dreaded the idea of having to go around again and battle other traffic in the pattern. I looked down ahead and somehow the field didn't look as if it was 1700 feet below, but much closer.

Then I gave the altimeter a quick glance and it read only 700 feet and I was lined up perfectly for the landing. I didn't have time to figure out what, if anything, I had done wrong, except misread the altimeter—a possibly fatal error. I was down now, over the threshold, and I flared out just a second too late because of my tired reactions and lack of skill. The plane touched down with a jolting bump on all three wheels. I grimaced, thinking how the boys in the control tower must have enjoyed watching the landing.

144

Anyone Can Fly

Wearily, I taxied to the tie-down area. My sense of triumph had been cheated by the rough weather, by being cut off in the pattern, and by that altimeter mistake. Or had it? I had completed another big hurdle under trying conditions. I'd used good sense, eluding a dangerous storm; I'd flown the trip in rough air and kept an altitude and heading and found my way.

As I got out of the plane, I glanced to the east, back toward New England, where the sky was still a rich, menacing black, and felt a little better. I dragged my damp carcass into the office where Tom sat eyeing me cryptically, like a doctor in an emergency room. He listened sympathetically; he pointed out little errors, and by now I'd guessed myself what had happened. Worn out by the turbulent air, I'd had to make a steep, climbing turn which had produced the onset of disorientation, just enough to misread the altimeter, but fortunately not enough to throw off my basic sense.

While I gulped some coffee, I told Tom I felt like doing some air work—I hadn't been satisfied with my turns or approaches. He looked at me the way Einstein would have glanced at a student who had just discovered the slide rule and said quietly, "How long have you been up?"

"Nearly three hours," I answered.

"That's plenty for one day. . . . You're too tired to absorb any more. I just had a student up for three hours and he kept insisting on more after the first hour, so I went along with him, but he wasn't getting anything out of it. You can only absorb so much in a given period of flying before your reactions and perceptions become dulled."

I knew enough not to disagree with Tom and started out toward my car. Suddenly, on the hot asphalt, my legs were like lead and I stumbled the last fifty steps. It occurred to me that if I'd flown nonstop from Los Angeles to Teterboro, I couldn't have been any more exhausted. I must have been tired—the Volkswagen engine cranking over with its inimitable bulldozer clatter actually sounded quiet.

Chapter Twelve. THE WRITTEN TEST

After you've flown your solo cross-country, and have the 25 hours of solo and 20 hours of dual required for your private license, you're ready for the private pilot's written test, a hurdle which must be passed before any student pilot is eligible to take his flight test and win his license. To paraphrase the song, "there *have* been some changes made." In the year that passed between the time we took our tests, the length, scope and complexity of the written exam had broadened. The reason: FAA's safety drive. The test has been made a bit more difficult to be sure that it can't be passed with pure luck. Passing it requires a comprehensive knowledge of everything you've learned as a student pilot.

Some characters walk away calling it a cut-and-dried affair. It is, too; it leaves you all cut up and feeling dried out. For most would-be pilots, the written test is a monstrous ogre, a three-hour session with the devil, and failing the test is a traumatic shock that reduces one's status in birdmanship.

It means having to admit to fellow pilots that you haven't learned quite well enough, and also means you'll have to wait another thirty days or get an instructor's approval to retake it. Lest the failure become too much of a worry, just remember that some of the best pilots around failed the test the first time they took it, and went back the second time around better equipped with flying expertise for a new try. Some of those who passed by the skin of their teeth never quite do find out just what they didn't know and, as a result, never have as much general knowledge as the man who went back for a second try.

The written test is meant to judge your knowledge of the rules and regulations set up by the FAA for weather, map work, flight planning, and all of the material available to the pilot that is necessary to safe pilotage. It seems tough, and it *is,* but it can be passed without an ordeal. The FAA says there are no trick questions and there are none. The trick is to know exactly how to find the answer on your computer or on paper, exactly how to use your *Airman's Guide,* Flight Information Manual, the back of the SAC charts, weather reports and general knowledge you're supposed to be equipped with when you enter. Within a three-hour period you must answer fifty questions, and thirty-five of these must have the correct answer to get a grade of 70 or a better passing mark.

There are several ways to make sure you have the upper hand. First, the United States Department of Commerce prints a series of pamphlets that are a must. They can be ordered through the Superintendent of Documents, United

States Government Printing Office, Washington 25, D.C., or you may be able to purchase them at your local airport, where they are generally stocked for the convenience of the students.

The titles of these booklets are *Realm of Flight, Path of Flight* and *Facts of Flight,* and they're priced between fifty and seventy-five cents each. After purchasing these, get your CAR (Civil Air Regulations) pamphlet with definitions and interpretations, and also order *Questions and Answers for Private Pilots* from the Government Printing Office. You have several additional choices. An approved ground school should never be passed over if you have the time and extra money. Or a few questions asked of your instructor will lead you to a good study guide such as the *Zwing Manual* or *Fowler's Guide.*

You can also form your own study group, getting together with three or four other fliers who are seriously interested in doing better than just passing on the test. Keep at it as regularly as at your flying until you know your stuff.

That last sentence is the clue to success. Studying for the written test is a serious job. The material you digest is important and cannot be done just once-over lightly. There is always the joker who says, "It's a snap! I just skimmed . . . [one book] and passed." He either has a photographic memory or likes to hear himself talk. Conversely, if you've really used your time well, studying and making sure you understand everything you memorized, you'll have the right to say that 60 per cent of the answers are right in the material that is given you to work with.

You're given a complete weather map and information with a key and guide as you begin the test. The answers are there, if you've really learned how to find them. The chart is the same kind you'll use in every flight you will make, with the same information, but covering a different area of the nation. And there are no hidden meanings. All the specifications of the imaginary plane you "fly" in the test—its limitations, performance and operational guides—are clearly and simply stated. The test should not be a guessing game.

When you've decided that enough midnight oil has been burned, take the test. Get it out of the way. Remember that it can take as long as three weeks (but generally takes about ten days) to find out your grade, and there might be three weeks of perfect flying weather you're missing in which you could be preparing for the flight test instead of worrying about the written examination.

When you actually are ready to take the test, get an early start and plan to use all of the three hours; in rechecking your answers you may catch those one or two errors that mean the difference between passing or not. A thermos of coffee, or something to nibble if you're going to be there around lunch time, can be a welcome break. Take your plotter, computer and an extra long ruler. One leg on the test we took extended far longer than a plotter's length, and the ruler made it a good deal easier to get an accurate bearing the first time around. Scratch paper and pencils will be supplied, but a few extra sharp pencils may come in handy.

The flight plan that day will go something like this: arrive sometime after nine. The only thing to check is that it is not a legal holiday. You need not make an appointment to take the test. You sign in. This means your name and time of arrival, as well as your status (student pilot), and whether you went to ground school. You will be given several sheets of scratch paper, a pencil, an answer sheet to be filled in, the exam booklet containing the questions, a sectional map, a weather map and reports, excerpts of the *Airman's Guide* and Flight Information tion Manual and an airplane flight manual for the plane you will be flying for the test. You will be allowed to keep all tools necessary for plotting a course. Reference material you bring along will be left on a table other than the one you will be using. One reference aid you can keep with you is the weather symbol guide, which will be supplied on request. Open up the exam booklet. You have three hours, more than an adequate amount of time. A suggestion made by Dick Klause, one of the top FAA examiners at Teterboro, is: "Read the questions *carefully*. More errors are made through *misinterpreting* the questions than in giving wrong answers. If a question confuses you, leave it blank. Come back to it. You'll have more time if you don't hold yourself back."

We've italicized the right answers; the questions will be something like this:

When flying cross-country your best choice during preflight planning for VFR should be a Sectional, WAC or route chart with radio aid and a scale of 1:500,000. (1) *SAC* (2) WAC (3) radio facility (4) route chart.

The principal source of weather conditions between reporting stations is from: (1) weather sequence reports (2) *pilot reports en route* (*PIREPS*) (3) FAA control towers (4) commercial broadcasting stations.

For information about maintenance service, types of fuel, lighting facilities, etc., that is available at airports of intended landing, check: (1) FAA manual (2) FAA Form 337 (3) Flight Information Manual (4) *Airman's Guide*.

Your home airport has an altitude of 2000 feet above sea level. As you leave you set your altimeter to its present reading of 29.75 as relayed from the control tower. Your next intended airport is 3500 feet above sea level. If you don't reset your altimeter to the reported reading of 30.25 on landing, your altitude would read approximately (1) 2000 feet (2) 2500 feet (3) *3000 feet* (4) 4000 feet.

As part of preflight planning, you correct your known true course for wind drift, variation and deviation. The result of these corrections is: (1) *compass heading* (2) magnetic heading (3) true heading (4) compass course.

Wind speed in weather reports is relayed in (1) either knots or miles per hour (2) miles per hour (3) *knots per hour* (4) kilometers.

In level flight at a steady airspeed (1) thrust exceeds gravity (2) thrust exceeds drag (3) *lift equals gravity* (4) lift exceeds the weight of an airplane.

Your weather reports warn of considerable moisture in the air and a check of temperature shows that conditions are favorable for icing. Therefore in flight you should (1) Apply full carburetor heat and leave it on. (2) *Apply carburetor heat at short intervals to check for icing.* (3) Use carburetor heat as soon as the engine coughs. (4) Seek an altitude less favorable to icing.

While in flight you hit an area of turbulence, so you slow your speed to one where sudden changes in attitude can be made more safely. This speed is designated as: (1) never-exceed speed (2) flap speed (3) *maneuvering speed* (4) maximum structural cruising speed.

The exam includes a simulated cross-country flight in which you must show your knowledge of radio aids; map skill, accurately computing a course with regard to time, winds, fuel consumption, landmarks; in general a comprehensive understanding of almost any situation you might encounter actually flying cross-country. And therefore it is not unreasonable to assume that you can pass it on paper before you apply it in action.

If you feel all wrung-out after the test, don't give it a second thought—almost everyone always is. That wrung-out feeling generally means you've done all right. It's the character who comes out fresh as a daisy, muttering, "That's a *test?*" who's usually in trouble. . . .

Chapter Thirteen. FLIGHT TEST: "TICKET TO TOMORROW"

You've now gone through the emotional wring-out of the written test, and you've passed. The next step is your actual flight test, and it's the last step before getting your private license—assuming that you pass it. And it, too, is a major experience. Here's the way it was for one young fledgling pilot—the actual experience, as described by my wife, Joanne. You'll find that you will share many of her experiences and reactions.

The appointment for the flight test was for 2:30 in the afternoon. The weather was perfect. Little or no wind, unlimited ceiling and 15-mile visibility. 10 A.M. The kids are playing. Over a cup of coffee, I rescanned the check list for the test that the FAA had compiled. My flight case contained pencils and scratch pad, a flight simulator, a local sectional chart, a Weems plotter, a Jeppesen CSG–1A computer, a small ruler, *Airman's Guide,* and pilot's logbook, containing medical certificate, radio license, student license and instructor's recommendation for my "ticket"—the coveted private pilot's license. I went over my notes from the written test, especially the CAR (civil air regulations). Turning over the map, I made a complete visual check of everything on the reverse side. It listed all the local omni's and their Morse code identification call and letters. 11 A.M. The baby-sitter arrived. Before leaving, I called weather and then checked what I could see. For a change there was no deception; it would be a perfect day. Good-bye to little faces for a while.

Then I made the drive to our local airport, intending to do a little practice flying before attempting the actual thing. Again I checked to see that the plane had its proper credentials: the engine and airframe logs, the radio licensing, the certificate of airworthiness, and the owner's and operator's manual. All was in order. It was now noon. This had taken ten minutes; a quick memory check of empty and full weights of the plane and the rate and angle of climb of the plane and another long ten minutes had dragged by.

You just can't judge time on the ground; nor can you sit there building up for this thing. So I got on the phone, made a quick call to FAA at Teterboro, and the appointment was upped to 1 P.M. I took off after one more call, again checking weather.

Once aloft, the first thing I did was to check the wind sock angle to the Hudson River. If you're ever really lost when flying in this area of the country, just head due east until you sight the Hudson River or the Atlantic Ocean. From there you should be able to find an easy landmark to check against. Another thing I've found helpful in any kind of flying: even if you know where your wind is coming from, orient yourself to some prominent landmark as soon as you're airborne. Unless there is a drastic wind shift, this initial reference solidifies your awareness of the prevailing wind.

I had a slight tailwind. I could just feel the wind stirring out of the northwest and knew I'd be using runway 6. But over Oradell Reservoir, I called the Teterboro tower and received landing instructions. I made my next call to the tower when I was on my downwind leg for runway 6. I always become so engrossed in the mechanics of getting my plane down that it wasn't until I had to ask for taxi instructions that I was conscious again of what lay ahead. This was it! I had been rained out once, obliged to baby-sit another time, and had such a bad case of nerves the third time that both the inspector and I had agreed this was not the day to even attempt the test.

I parked the plane and double-checked all switches, took a deep breath and started up the stairs to the FAA office. I was told that an Al Dessert was the man to give me my check ride. I let his name go by without any puns (I was sure he had heard them all), and his comment on my rather lengthy log was simply: "Well, you *should* know how to fly her." We shook hands and started out on the 3½-hour check ride on a first-name basis.

The first part was almost routine. I handed over my log, medical certificate, radio license, student ticket, score from the written test and my instructor's recommendation that I was okay for the flight test. This was followed by my engine log, airframe log, radio licensing, certificate of airworthiness, owner's and operator's manual and another deep breath.

Then I was on my own. How often is a plane inspected? (Every twelve months.) What happens with four passengers and sixty pounds of luggage and full fuel tanks? (You're overweight—throw out luggage or some fuel; passengers have a habit of being disappointed.) In-flight frequencies? (Transmit and listen on 121.5 for emergency only; 121.7 or 121.9 for ground control; 122.5 for the tower for transmitting, and receive on the frequency found on the map—if you don't have the correct transmitting crystal; and, of course, 122.8 or 123.0 for Unicom.)

How much gas? (Eighteen gallons in each tank.) And how much does it weigh? (Six pounds per gallon.) Stalling speed? (Forty-nine miles per hour without flaps.) What happens when a plane is overloaded? (The center of gravity shifts and the stall speed increases.) Best angle of climb and best attitude of climb? (Referred to operator's manual.)

I answered as fast as I could, guessed the best I could on what I wasn't sure of, and asked to refer to the operator's manual. The best answer, when you don't know, is knowing where to find out in a hurry.

The examiner doesn't expect you to be a walking flying-encyclopedia, but he wants to be sure that you know your plane, what it can do safely at its best and at its worst. He wants to know that you can get answers when there isn't an instructor around to turn to.

Next we spread out a New York Sectional and he asked me to point out a control area, control zone, omni station, low frequency station, and a climb corridor.

He instructed me to plot a course from Teterboro, north to Anderson Acres and to Danbury in Connecticut, then back to Teterboro.

Then he left me to my own methods armed with the tools I had brought. Of all the silly word combinations such as "West is best and East is least" (for your variation corrections), and *"ci*g*a*rets *f*or *t*he *p*ilot's *r*est" (*c*ontrols, *i*nstruments, *g*as, *f*laps, *t*rim, *p*rop, *r*un-up), I unabashedly adhere to the unforgettable slogan "*t*rue *v*irgins *m*ake *d*ull *c*ompany" (*t*rue course, *v*ariation, *m*agnetic course, *d*eviation, *c*ompass course) for the best method of remembering the business of plotting a course.

I pulled out an FAA flight planning card and was halfway through filling out a blank flight plan when Al said, "Okay, let's go." He added that we would assume weather to be clear and winds negligible—as was the case.

It was with pride that I walked over to One Zero Zulu. I had polished her windows with great care. Even though she had over a hundred hours on her, she had that brand-new, clean look. I felt almost guilty about confessing that there was a slight error in her altimeter. But Al agreed with me that I should adjust it to a sea level reading and note the correction that would be necessary.

When preflighting a plane I like to start from the right door and come around back to it. I followed the routine with exceptional care, being cautious. But as I said earlier, Al Dessert, as the examiner, was there as much to help as to find out if you were really a qualified pilot.

When I came to my engine check, he added fine points such as where to check for strained engine mounts in case of a hard landing, the ground wires for the mags, the fuel primer lines and their importance. When we came to the tail section and I had finished my check, he again pointed out that the strut was held to the stabilizer by a single angled piece of metal, and that although this weakness had been corrected in all recent models, it was critical pieces such as this that really needed careful inspection.

Now I was joined in the cockpit by Al, who was really my first passenger (a pretty critical one at that), even though at the time if he had called himself this, I would have nervously (*very* nervously) laughed. Ground control cleared us, and we taxied into position for my run-up. 2:10 P.M. The run-up completed, I switched to tower frequency and received my instructions for takeoff.

A clean run, fast lift-off, and: "One Zero Zulu leaving pattern."

"Have a good trip, One Zero Zulu."

I circled the field to gain altitude and get directly on course and started my cross-country flight according to plan. My friend, the nonwandering Hudson River, was clearly in view; I checked wind direction again off the Hudson. There was a slight quartering head wind. Mentally and physically, I adjusted to it.

Visibility was so lovely that the next checkpoints, Suffern and the New City Reservoir, were visible almost from the moment I reached my altitude of 2500 feet. Just as I was about to feel good about things, my passenger jarred me back to the harsh reality of the test.

"You've just been weathered in and want a field with a tower to fly to———"

"Westchester!" I popped out quickly.

Again jarringly, he came back with, "Well, what are you wasting time about? Why haven't you changed your course?"

After a quick examination of the map spread across my lap, I knew that a 95° turn right and a 90° course across the Hudson was the line of attack. Another check of my map and I switched my radio from Teterboro tower to 118.5 for Westchester County. A sly glance and I knew that thus far I had been successful. My left hand, however, was a sweating paw. My wedding band was cutting right into my palm. I pulled it off and was desperately looking for a place to put it when Al took it and, as if this were a boringly routine occurrence, placed it on the empty end of the ignition key ring.

Now came my turn to prove my skill with One Zero Zulu. "Slow fly at 75 miles per hour!" Set your throttle just right and trim her up, she'll do it herself. Remember she needs a touch of right rudder.

"Make clearing turns while in slow flight," I reminded myself—first 90° to the right and then 90° to the left, back to where we started from. Watch your altitude and maintain 75 mph.

"Resume cruising speed and make a 720 to the right!"

Back to my friend, the Hudson again. I faced One Zero Zulu toward the river and found a spot downwind to use as my starting point.

"Talking her" into the maneuver, I poured One Zero Zulu into the bank, checked altitude, turn and bank indicator, set the throttle a little higher and went round and round. Line up that windshield strut across the horizon and maintain a level turn on the rate-of-climb indicator; check rpm and manifold pressure; make a visual check to see how far around you've flown . . . 360° . . . back across the dash again.

"Okay, see that island in the lake? Make a left pylon around it."

This was suddenly like doing a swan dive and changing to a backward flip in mid-air. I just hoped it wouldn't turn into a belly-flop. I congratulated myself on my luck that it was a left pylon and not a right, or I would have been lost. Somehow I got around, noticed I had lost 60 feet, and pulled her nose up as I came out of the turn and got her back to 2500 feet again. Next on the agenda were stalls. The first two times around I just mushed the old Tri-Pacer through. The third time I got good and mad, used both hands and spanked her into it. Then Al took over, very nicely doing the most beautiful maneuvers I've ever seen One Zero Zulu put through. It was a pleasure to be there with him.

He handed the controls back to me and told me to go into a stall with full flaps, both notches. The only flap left was my open jaw. This was a new maneuver for me. Again, he demonstrated and I followed through. His handling of the plane was becoming contagious; I performed a smooth maneuver and then stalls were over. 2:45 P.M.

The more maneuvers he put me through the more I understood what he was trying to find out about my flying. I had done better air work with my instructor, *but never had I been more careful.* I knew that he wanted me to demonstrate to him that I knew how to handle this plane safely and surely all the time. He didn't expect me to be able to fly formation in a squadron of Air Force pilots, but he did expect me to know *every* rule of safety, not just the basic ones.

"Climb to 3000 feet." I did so, repeating my pattern of clearing turns all the way, so I would be ready for anything he asked for. "Why not above 3000 feet?" he queried.

"Controlled air." Just above the Spring Valley area is an intersection for La-Guardia Airport above 3000 feet, and we were in an area that always has a good deal of air traffic.

I trimmed One Zero Zulu for straight-and-level flight, once more clearing myself for the next routine on the test, which was gliding. I went into turns, floating straight down and then soaring back up in graceful climbs, remembering to constantly clear the engine by easing the throttle in and out again and using my carburetor heat at all times. To me, glides have always been the most pleasant part of flying. Once you have her trimmed up well and you have the right nose attitude, the sudden quiet, with no engine booming and the low dull sound with the throttle pulled almost all the way back, gives me a real sense of flight.

The time for these routines was just perfect for me. I needed a few minutes to once more get real control of the situation and, in a way, to reassure myself for the next step, which I knew had to be under the hood. We finished this whole segment with no repeat maneuvers needed, and pulled her back to 2500 feet, ready to move on. 3:00 P.M.

Al took over the controls while I put on the hood. He trimmed her up again beautifully. So by the time I was blinded to the terrain about me, Madame Zulu was flying herself. He placed a map over the windshield and away I went. I flew her straight-and-level on a given course. I climbed her and let her down; I turned to given course, left and then right. Then 360s and 180s.

"Take it easy on the rudder . . . watch out for too steep climbs . . . watch that airspeed . . . what's the altimeter doing? . . . shallow the bank." Some were his reminders, some mine.

I was skidding in a turn; I corrected. I pulled out the carburetor heat too often, but better safe than sorry. I overshot one turn by 10° and overcorrected by 15°. But I maintained altitude, got to my heading and once there held it.

Then it was his turn to shake me up again. He asked for the controls and proceeded to juggle the plane about as if she'd just been thrown into a thunderhead. Smack in the middle, he said, "Okay, it's yours." If you were to ask me one minute later what attitude we had been in, I couldn't have answered.

All I remember is that I wanted her straight and level. I visually ran across the dash: airspeed first, then my horizon; wings leveled out now, and then the Tri-Pacer's nose back where it belonged. I'm sure she looked a lot more like a Yo-yo on a string than a plane for about three seconds. But I did it, and correctly, until she settled down.

"Now," he said, "I'm going to put her in a dive and I want you to get her out of it." I knew what was going to happen, and thought this should be easy. But again, he swung her around, put her into a steep climb and several sharp turns before banking off into a dive to the right. My instructor had put in a deadman's spin attitude under the hood and this didn't feel that much different.

My first reaction was to pull back the throttle to cut speed. It took all I had to just sit on the nose until she came up, for she started to yaw; and even though the Tri-Pacer has bungee controls, she needed a good deal of extra rudder. I found the nose almost in a stall attitude by the time I realized that I had to use the artificial horizon instead of the rate-of-climb indicator. I had lost quite a bit of altitude, and a good deal of my orientation before getting her level, but level she was. As I started to retrim, Al removed the hood and said again, "Watch the rudders and don't *overcontrol*. This plane likes to right itself."

He took over the controls while I just relaxed for a moment. 3:25 P.M.

He handed me the map and told me to cross-check two omni's while I was sitting and find out where we were. It's easy to work omni while someone else is at the controls, but again, he was not out to see what I could do as if I were a fully accomplished radioman. I checked Poughkeepsie and Wilton and pinpointed us on a map, looked out the window, and that was where we were. No one was more surprised than me.

All the time we were flying, he kept asking questions like, "Why do you want to fly? How long has your husband been flying? How many children have you? Where do you live?" always finding out really whether I could handle both flying the plane and carrying on a conversation with a passenger, I guess.

Only once did I tell him to be quiet and that was on our next and final part of this flight test. He wanted me to demonstrate a short field landing and spot landing combination. What better choice than Ramapo Valley Airport? On final, he asked about something or other and I just completely ignored him. I wasn't sure of his reaction. When we were about to touchdown, he took over and said, "Let's keep going." I turned to him apologetically (I don't know why) and explained that landing a plane was a full-time occupation for me and that no small talk was to be engaged in.

Maybe the message had been too strongly put. I hopefully thought that he smiled as he said simply, "That's fine. Now head back for Teterboro." The winds had not changed. I now had a tail wind again rather than a head wind. I called Teterboro and received pattern instructions. Then I turned to Al and said weakly, "Well, who buys the coffee?" I didn't have the courage to ask outright if I had passed the test.

All he answered was, "Make this a *good* landing." I still didn't know. The traffic was quite heavy as usual at Teterboro. I entered downwind and had her throttled back for slow flying and trimmed up. I held 800 feet as if I were on a level road 800 feet up in the sky. I received clearance to turn base. Just as I was turning, an Aeronca cut in and under. I was mad. I called the tower and told them I was dragging out my downwind leg until I found out just what that *other* winged beast was doing.

Once again I was cleared for base, and I watched the Aeronca circle the field as I entered final. It was 3:50 P.M.

"One Zero Zulu on final for full stop," I declared with great finality. I had plenty of room to let her down slowly and evenly. She touched ground right after a darn near perfect flare out. It was beautiful. I rolled down to the taxi strip, turned off and switched to ground control, asking permission to park. I followed the lineman's wigwagging, turned her around, put on the brake, leaned out the fuel, cut my mags off, then cut the master switch, still waiting to hear about a coffee invitation. Finally, I said again, "Well, who buys the coffee?"

"Right after I sign the papers we'll see if we have time. Congratulations."

Chapter Fourteen. LICENSED, LEGAL: LOOK OUT, OR NANTUCKET, HERE WE COME

Weeks after you've passed your flight and written tests, a small, white photostated card arrives in your mail—your private pilot's license, marked with the type of aircraft "Airplane—Single Engine—Land" that you have qualified to fly. You'll have already been flying on your own; the FAA flight examiner will have filled out a postflight temporary license and noted in your logbook, "Private pilot's flight test—all standards met," and signed it with his name and examiner's number.

With your private ticket, you're now able to take up your friends, family or anybody that will trust you. Like as not, most of your friends will still view you with suspicion; it may take them months to come around to the point where they'll allow you to get them into the airplane. This time isn't exactly lost, since you'll be getting better and, most of all, convincing yourself that you *are* qualified to take them up. There somehow exists a fine point of difference in the minds of most new pilots between risking their own hides and involving anybody else.

And this is all to the good, because the period between getting your license when you have, say, 50 to 70 hours of flying time, until you get up to about 200 hours of flying time, is probably the most dangerous time. It's a time when you learn a lot about yourself as well as about your flying, a time when you develop safe flying habits.

You have your license, you've learned the basics of weather and you now automatically begin to coordinate all your knowledge in terms of *go* or *no go*. As with missile-launching at Cape Kennedy, the *go* status, which is vital, means that you, the weather and the airplane are really all right to take off.

Most of the time the *go* will involve the weather: is it really good enough now? Will it stay good enough for me to get where I'm flying to and make it back? And it sometimes becomes a race against time, especially when you get involved in the game with fast-moving weather systems, or with a combination of marginal local conditions that are likely to be complicated within hours by a fast-moving system.

You can get caught, as we have been, even after you have gotten your license.

Everybody does, including commercial jet pilots and crack military pilots. The trick is to know *what to do* and *when to do it* if you do get caught. We didn't— at some unhappy point everybody doesn't. You should.

It was a Fourth of July weekend and we'd decided to fly up to Nantucket to escape the heat and humidity of New York. Bright and early Saturday, we checked our friendly FAA operatives at Poughkeepsie radio range. From New York to Nantucket, the weather looked good, though not spectacularly clear. Bridgeport, for example, reported: scattered clouds at 3000 feet, and visibility 6 miles in smoke. Nantucket was reporting broken cloudiness at 2500 feet, visibility 4 miles. Best of all, it was expected to pick up during the day and be as good, if not better, the next day when we'd be flying back. Prediction: fair skies, seasonable temperatures and fine swimming. Far to the west, a cold front was sweeping in, but not as yet moving very fast.

We filed a VFR flight plan and took off from Ramapo Valley at 11 A.M. Climbing at the Tri-Pacer's best ascent speed (95 mph), we reached 2500 feet as we crossed into Westchester over the Hudson. The air was warm and soggy, but not bumpy. It was immediately apparent that the ceiling was lower than the weather people were reporting*; it had changed quickly since their last observation. We were running into broken, not scattered, clouds at 3000 feet and the bottoms of some of them stuck down close to 2500 feet. No problem as yet, just a bit of threading around to stay out of the bottoms of the clouds and not get any lower than 2500 feet.

* Weather is sort of like radar speed traps: you never know quite where they—or it—will be next, so you're best staying legal – and safe – by always calculating what conditions look like ahead.

The Connecticut Turnpike, like most United States superhighways, is an unbeatable landmark.

It was a sunny VFR day and flying up along the Connecticut shore there was no need to use the plane's VOR or LF radio navigation equipment. We kept the VOR tuned in, cranking it to each station as we passed within its range. Since we'd filed a VFR flight plan from Ramapo Valley with Poughkeepsie radio, we reported our progress as we went along—to Bridgeport tower, Hartford radio and then to Providence.

By the time we'd passed New London and were over Rhode Island, the broken clouds reached down to 2000 feet, the air was getting a bit bumpy and we were getting uncomfortable. The idea of crossing the width of Buzzards Bay at low altitude, then having to cover 14 miles of open water between Martha's Vineyard and Nantucket again at 1500 or 2000 feet in a single-engine plane didn't appeal to me. We had no life preservers aboard, and if the engine conked out, 2000 feet didn't offer half enough gliding distance to make it to land.

Over Westport Point, on the lower Massachusetts shore, we turned out over Buzzards Bay, reporting this first to Providence radio, then tuning in to Nantucket radio. We locked onto Nantucket's clear, strong omni-range signal, centered the needle and headed on out. There was just one trouble: we were barely able to make out Martha's Vineyard, only three or four miles offshore, and the cloud deck now had us down to 1500 feet. But we did have the safety of the small islands between the mainland and Martha's Vineyard, so we pushed on.

Reaching the shore of Martha's Vineyard, it really got sticky. The ceiling was down to 1000 feet and the island was lost in a thick haze, a lovely potpourri of leftover fog from the night before and ripening morning-after clouds.

As we crossed just south of the main Martha's Vineyard Airport, I'd already

Crossing Martha's Vineyard just south of Gay Head.

cranked the radio over to Unicom to talk to old Steve Gentle, then running Katama Airport in Edgartown (where we'd gotten some of our first love of flying). We figured that if Nantucket looked too sticky we'd land at Edgartown and spend the day swimming there. Calling Steve produced static, blooping sounds and a mess of cross talk; I never did hear him, though later he told us he heard our plane all right. As we passed near the air park, my altimeter read 700 feet. We could see the shore and a trace of water, but not a sign of Nantucket, 14 miles in the distance. It was a day for surf-bathing, not cloud-dunking.

Just for kicks, we crossed out to the tip of Martha's Vineyard, circling to land at Edgartown if it looked too bad. Gadzooks! There looked like a small hole; one more circle and there wasn't a cloud in sight for 50 miles. Nantucket glistened brightly in the distance, the ocean was beyond; suddenly ceiling and visibility were unbelievably good.

Within ten minutes we were in the pattern at Nantucket Memorial Airport; in twelve minutes we were on the ground; and in thirty minutes, we'd found lodgings and were headed for the beach, after first fueling the Tri-Pacer and getting her safely tied down for the night.

Stopping in to say hello to the Weather Bureau people at the airport produced more good news: the front was expected to stay away from the New York area until after dark tomorrow, so we'd be able to make it back easily. We'd made plans to meet another flying friend and went next door to the FAA radio office to ask if they'd gotten a call from his plane.

Banking for Edgartown Airport on the tip of the Vineyard.

"Wait a minute," the FAA man declared, after first saying he'd not heard from the ship. "Do you mean Cessna —— Charlie?"

"None other," we answered.

"That maniac," he said between gritted teeth, "came over here the other night in a pouring rainstorm. It was so bad that not even the seagulls, much less the Convairs, were flying."

We promptly filed and forgot his words and spent the day sunning, swimming and forgetting about fronts.

At 8 A.M. the next morning, we called our friendly weatherman and got the first bad news of the day. Nantucket was wide open, high ceiling and visibility, but the entire mainland was locked in by fog, smoke, haze and generally unspeakable conditions.

"Providence," the man declared bitterly, "is for driving only today; they're calling 600 feet and a half-mile in fog." The story was the same down the line. We were trapped. Things were supposed to slowly improve, but that cold front was now moving faster and they were predicting it would strike the New York area by 5 P.M. It would be a tight squeeze, and we had to be back in New York that night.

The weather in Martha's Vineyard was still good, however, so we decided to hop over there, see how things looked, say hello to Steve, and if the fog still looked bad, get Steve (a crack instructor and instrument pilot) to fly us back to New York.

On the ground at Nantucket Airport. "All right, so he's got *two* engines, but he only goes 25 miles an hour faster than us. . . ."

We took off, headed straight for Edgartown and called in. More mumbo jumbo with the "Mickey Mouse" radio in the Tri-Pacer. Once I heard Steve, then lost him. The Vineyard itself now was just about VFR—visibility barely 3 miles and ceiling about 2000 feet. And the land mass of the United States to the west was lost in junk. We made ready to land.

Just then the radio, still cranked to Unicom, 122.8 mc., came alive: "Tri-Pacer One Zero Zulu . . . do you read Cessna —— Charlie?" Our friend, with the submarine-type airplane, was finally showing up. We talked back and forth; he was going to Hyannis. "How is the weather coming up?" we asked.

"Well, . . ." He hemmed and hawed. "It's not very nice, but it's still okay. You can make it if you start right now."

We decided to at least try past Martha's Vineyard, then turn back if it looked too bad. Both of us, my friend and myself, should have known better. The man in question is one of the best pilots I know, but he does take chances—too many chances. (Including one he didn't know about until he read this book—having writers for friends!)

We called Nantucket radio and filed a flight plan for New York, telling them we were going to give it a try. The man sounded slightly amazed, but took our plan and asked us to call in when we reached the mainland.

As we left Martha's Vineyard, we caught sight of the Rhode Island shore; eternal optimists, we decided to make a run for the mainland. We tuned to Providence VOR and headed for the shore at 1500 feet. We should then and there have had our heads examined. Because we never really found the shore, or more exactly, never discovered at what point we reached the shore. We saw land below and headed south for New York. I bent over to retune the radio from Providence to Hartford while Joanne worked with the maps, trying to discover where we were. At that point I would have rated the ceiling 1000 feet and the visibility at two

No question about it: it's a dirty, no-good rain cloud.

miles. The reliable radio wasn't able to pull in Hartford, some 70 miles away, at such a low altitude, and I tuned again to Quonset Point, the Navy range, which couldn't have been more than 15 miles away.

When I looked up from the radio panel, it was into the face of a solid mass of clouds surrounding me, with no visibility in front of me. We dropped down through the last hole remaining and found ourselves flying at 600 feet and hardly able to maintain it. The visibility at best might have been one-quarter of a mile.

"Land! you idiot!" I told myself. Concealing her panic, Joanne feverishly looked from map to land, trying to pick out a landmark.

Quonset Point VOR failed to come in at all. Calling them on the radio produced no answer. Later, we found that Quonset, like a fair number of military bases, sometimes doesn't bother to answer calls on VHF frequencies. When we desperately tried to call them on the emergency frequency, 121.5 mc., we still got nothing.

Now we knew we were lost. We'd flown inland from the shore several miles trying to pick up a landmark without luck. All we saw below us, and not very far below us, were small farms, scattered homes, and country roads too narrow to set the Tri-Pacer down on. We circled a few times and were lucky enough to come out over a body of water we thought looked like Newport Bay. But if it was Newport Bay, the air station that should have been down there failed to turn up. There was only one thing to do, we figured—turn back to our original course heading for New York, and see if we could find a hole and an open field to land in.

Two hundred and thirty degrees. 120 mph. 600 feet altitude; then 500 . . . 400 . . . 300 . . . the deck of thick stratocumulus clouds pushed down on us until the ground below—which fortunately was very flat, with no high towers anywhere near on the map—seemed to reach out for us.

From 300 feet, I picked out more farmhouses, ominous two-lane highways strewn with telephone poles, and rocky fields. Not a single place to land. And we dared not fly any farther at this low altitude—after all, we might take off somebody's television antenna. It was a time for action; and the decision, like all desperate acts, was difficult to make; the lives we might lose were our own. All we kept thinking was that if we only had our instrument ratings we could have climbed over this junk and flown back neatly to New York.

Looking up, I spotted a fair-sized hole in the clouds, and made what would have been the wrong decision in any other instance. I decided to climb through the hole—which looked just like the familiar inviting "sucker" hole—rather than attempt to crash-land the plane below. Full power now, with the throttle at 2600 rpm. The Tri-Pacer shuddered, and soared ahead, building speed, then I pulled back and sailed her up through the hole, fully expecting to be trapped above a solid layer of clouds. Not only was this illegal by every rule in the book for a VFR pilot, but it was also possible to get stuck trying to descend through such a solid mass and to lose the plane in the clouds.

Fifteen hundred feet—the sky seemed to be getting a bit brighter. At 1800 feet we suddenly broke out into another world, a free clean world with hope. We were between two decks. Below and disappearing behind us, was the solid mass of stratocumulus we'd gotten caught in; above, a thin layer of scattered clouds at about 3500 feet. Ahead were layers of smoke, haze and bits of fog—it was just barely VFR, but the shore line appeared in view. The ceiling was slowly lifting.

The time was 3 P.M. and the man on the radio kept warning us about the approaching cold front.

It was an idiotic afternoon: we'd be flying along with bare visibility minimums and suddenly it would drop down to a half-mile or one mile, then pick up again. Then there would be brief showers. But we droned and groaned along toward New York, ducking to the side of thicker clouds, scooting past cumulus "builds" that had begun to appear. Curiously, the radio seemed barren of other pilots. When we called Hartford, then Bridgeport, the men seemed happy to have somebody to talk to. They also seemed a bit surprised to find us jogging along on a VFR flight plan, since most VFR fliers had given it up as a lost cause early in the day.

We turned inland a bit over Wilton VFR, called in and headed straight for Ramapo Valley. Now we could see the front, big, black and frightening, straight ahead to the west. It looked far enough away for us to make it, but we weren't sure.

The radio crackled with a flash advisory for the New York area: "Severe thunderstorms, hail and rain after 1700 Greenwich." I looked at my watch: it was 4:30 P.M. EDT—1630 Greenwich. We were passing from Connecticut to Westchester, Ramapo Valley was now only about 40 miles, or 20 minutes, away. Joanne looked at me with a contemptuous "aren't you skillful because we're still alive" glance, and turned away. I advanced the throttle from 2350 rpm—cruising speed—to a blasting 2500 rpm. The airspeed needle crept up to about 127 mph.

Now the Hudson passed below us. We were flying at 2000 feet, so it wasn't necessary to make much of a descent. About ten miles to go. But the black front had suddenly boiled up quite close—perhaps 15 to 20 miles in the distance.

We cranked the radio in to Ramapo Valley and told them we were coming in. The wind had already picked up and the sock was blossoming out nervously when we hastily circled the field. The Tri-Pacer sailed back and forth and trembled in the blustery crosswind as we landed.

As we taxied up, the first drops of rain splattered on the windshield. When we tied faithful One Zero Zulu down, everybody was busy tying all the other ships down. One Zero Zulu's wings rocked in the stiffening breeze. I fondled her spinner and locked her up just as the sky opened up in a downpour.

That evening after the storm, my friend with the hurricane-hunting Cessna made it back.

"How was it coming down?" we asked.

"Oh, not bad," he calmly declared. "Visibility wasn't so hot in places, but it was no problem." No, I declared inwardly, not when you fly with your eyes closed.

"How did you find it?" he asked.

"Just great," I replied. "Clear all the way."

"What?" he started to ask, as I hung up.

It was the closest call we'd had in what now amounts to nearly five years of pretty intensive flying. We'd learned what weather really means—learned just short of the hard way. Next time—well, we resolved, there wouldn't be a next time because we'd never again allow ourselves to get that close to disaster.

The wrong decision is always the easier one.

Heat haze and lowered visibility make any airport welcome.

"All right, so it's a river, but *which* one?"

Anyone Can Fly   The wind sweeps in from the left. Dropping the left wing into it prevents the plane from drifting off course.

But the wind is not always constant, nor consistent: you've got to play it.

It's still crossed and you've got to hold the wing down.

Lined up straight down the runway and compensated for the crosswind.

Just a little more correction.

Always straighten the wing out just before touching down.

And a perfect landing.

Chapter Fifteen. UNDER THE HOOD— EYES IN THE NIGHT

A wall of white envelops you. You're flying into a great billowing white sea of cotton and, as it envelops your plane, you begin to get panicky. You're used to judging the attitude of the airplane by the horizon, which conveniently stays ahead of you, enabling you to stay ahead of the plane.

A moment ago you had a horizon; now it's suddenly lost in the churning white confusion of the cloud bank you've made the mistake of flying into. What do you do now?

The average private pilot, panicking but telling himself he had everything under control, used to be good for about eighty seconds more of life on this earth after getting lost in the clouds. For a few seconds, he'd fly on—then, with the wings level, he'd get the feeling he was in a steep bank. Quite normally, he'd try to level his wings and put the plane into a bank. But it doesn't work. He begins diving and pulling up so steeply he's nearly in a stall. Too late, he realizes his error, and desperately tries to take his eyes away from where the horizon used to be and to get his eyes glued onto the gyro horizon, and onto DG—the directional gyro compass. If he moved his eyes quickly enough, and knew how to use the instruments, he'd get himself out of trouble quickly enough.

But the average private pilot, a fair-weather Sunday pilot, doesn't know anything about instrument flying. Any time he exceeds his ability, by accident or deliberation, he gets himself into bad, bad trouble. Everybody knows the problem. The question is: what to do about it?

Moving forward into an era that bodes to be one of mass transportation by air, the Federal Aviation Agency has set out to meet the challenge of instrument training for the private flier and to get him out of problem weather. For years, instrument flying was an advanced technique—one which only really ambitious private fliers cared to spend the time and money learning.

But the number of accidents brought about by private fliers tackling or getting caught in bad weather continued to mount. Private planes have reliable engines and are well built. The weakness lay in inexperienced pilots getting involved in poor weather. The figures finally reached a point where a frighteningly large percentage of all private and business aircraft accidents were attributed to bad weather.

Early recognizing this problem, the Aircraft Owners And Pilots Association

(AOPA) came out with their life-saving 180° course. Simply stated, this was a move to imbue in pilots the judgment to turn around before getting into trouble. Or, if they did get caught, the 180° course was designed to give them the ability to make elementary use of their instruments in order to turn around, get out of the clouds and land in safety.

Now FAA had begun to meet the challenge. The revised Flight Test Guide for the Private Pilots Examination calls for the student to demonstrate his ability to maneuver the airplane in a "safe and positive" manner "solely by reference to the aircraft instruments."

With an instrument hood on, the student pilot—in a plane that has to have at least elementary instruments, such as turn-and-bank indicator, airspeed gauge and altimeter—must demonstrate his ability to:

1. Recover from the start of a power-on spiral.
2. Recover from the approach to a climbing stall.
3. Maneuver in normal turns of at least 180° left and right to within 20° of a preselected course heading.
4. Climb in a shallow turn to a predetermined altitude.
5. Descend at reduced power to a predetermined altitude.
6. Fly straight and level.
7. Perform a timed turn.

The instruction time necessary to acquire this rudimentary instrument-flying proficiency generally is about five hours. It is probably the best investment any flier can ever make. But for the cost, it is likely FAA would call on all private fliers to have their instrument rating. And it is not unlikely that in the future greater instrument-flight skill will be demanded by FAA before licensing private pilots.

A sounder long-range solution would seem to be to change the entire manner of flight instruction. A pioneering program by the University of Illinois Institute of Aviation called Simultaneous Contact-Instrument Training proved that students could be taught a combined course in order to get their private pilot license and at the same time also acquire basic instrument-flying skill. Nearly all of the students got their license with a combined total of less than 35 hours of flying time. The reason was that they were given a thorough preflight course including more than 13 hours of discussion, and 11 hours average time in a Link trainer, all administered by above-average instructors.

The conclusion, of course, was that all the students were better equipped to cope with unexpected instrument weather than the average private pilot. Because of the new FAA requirements, it is likely that most flight instructors are going to end up teaching a course identical in spirit—starting students from the beginning to use their instruments—even if they're unable to take advantage of Link trainer facilities.

Perhaps the best part is this: students who learn in such a manner know their own limitations and keep themselves out of trouble much more than those who've learned purely with visual flight methods.

The United States Army's Aviation Center is already embarked on a study using fifteen Cessna 180s to test the idea of combining visual and instrument flight instruction from the earliest stages of flight training.

Once you've gotten your license, and a taste of instrument flying, you'll want to go on to get your rating. Not only will your flying be safer, but you'll be able to fly under some nondangerous conditions under which the VFR flier can't get into the sky.

In elementary instrument training, the kind you'll get to ready yourself for the private pilot's ticket, here's what you'll face. After a normal takeoff and climb-out, your instructor will take you to a practice area. After you reach the area and a safe altitude of about 2500 feet, he'll tell you to put on the "hood," a black metal or plastic eye shield which cuts off your view of the sky and horizon and restricts your visibility to the instruments on the dashboard directly in front of you.

The first lesson is devoted to flying the plane straight-and-level on a given course. You'll find yourself learning more about exactly how your plane performs at given power settings and in winds than you dreamed possible. The compass will show you drifting left or right, of course—depending on the winds. You'll cut in too late with rudder to hold your course, but you've probably drifted so far off that the aileron is necessary to get back to the smaller limits controllable with rudder. After a half-hour or so, you'll get the exact feel of the plane on instruments—not the familiar seat-of-the-pants instinct, which is valid when you fly VFR but dead wrong for IFR. Seat-of-the-pants flying is downright misleading under instrument conditions. You begin to build faith in the truth of what your instruments tell you.

Under the hood.

Soon you'll have straight-and-level on-course work mastered. Then turns to new headings, all around the compass, rolling out exactly on the new course. After this, climbing and descending to new altitudes while changing course. Finally, basic timed turns, turning a given number of degrees within an exact amount of time—for example, a 30-second, 90° turn.

At first, all VFR pilots taking instrument instruction wildly overcontrol, and end up in dives, wild climbs approaching stalls, or overly steep banks. Ground school- or bookwork—studying the basic artificial horizon, directional gyro, and other key instruments—will give you the extra knowledge of how to stay ahead of the plane; you will *know,* not guess, what is happening. It takes a few hours to get the feel of rudimentary instrument-flying controlling, and then—with another pilot in the right-hand seat flying as "safety pilot," watching out for other planes— you go up and practice.

From this elementary training, which is enough to prove to the FAA that you have the know-how to get out of trouble if you get into it, you can move on up to your instrument rating. The basic training will get you FAA's "Blue Seal"—a stamped mark on your private pilot's ticket showing you have mastered the minimum instrument training.

The "Blue Seal" is now, thank goodness, mandatory for new pilots. Despite the gripes of a few that it raises the cost of learning how to fly, it's the best money you'll ever spend. This is because this basic IFR capability is an insurance policy for pilots: you invest some money and time to save your life if you ever get caught when ceilings are coming down, or sudden clouds surround you. Now you have the actual ability to get down through the clouds, safely do a 180° turn back to safety, or fly a triangular pattern to help others help you. And if necessary, you will be able to respond with some skill to radioed instrument instructions to talk you down.

If you keep on with instrument training, you'll learn how to do instrument landings—ILSs—using fields with ILS equipment, and GCAs with radar guidance from major fields, and also gain the ability to use your VHF navigation gear and LF radio range equipment to maximum advantage. In short, you're on your way to flying like a professional.

You may never have to actually use your newly developed IFR training, but it's mighty handy to have in the background ready to pull out in case of a tight squeak.

And there are few acts in flying as satisfying as a really good GCA approach. Miles away from the field you're going to land at you contact the GCA frequency and get on with a GCA controller, who then sets up your approach after identifying your position and the type of plane.

"Zero One X-Ray . . . come to new heading—two four zero." You turn right to the new heading. "Zero One X-Ray, descend to one thousand feet. . . ." Cutting back your power slightly, you begin a standard GCA descent to reach the new altitude. Now you're only two miles out from the field. New course headings and approach orders come fast over the radio until you find yourself on final— with the hood still on—in your simulated GCA approach.

"Zero One X-Ray . . . on course, on glide path . . ." tells you that your plane is lined up exactly with the center line of the runway you're due to touch down on, and that you're descending at the proper rate—on a line from the nose of the plane to a point safely beyond the threshold of the runway. Now the corrections are fine-grained: "Zero One X-Ray . . . come left to course one eight degrees . . . ten feet below glide path." You touch left rudder slightly . . . and move to the new heading . . . a slight amount of back pressure on the wheel—watching your airspeed closely—and you're back on the glide path.

Countless other fine adjustments ensue. "Course is good . . . glide path is good . . . on course, on glide path . . . you're over the threshold now, take over for visual landing."

You look up from the instruments and find your plane perfectly centered over the white line ten feet over the runway. GCA and radar have taken you in through the fog, haze, or low clouds until you can pick up with VFR technique and safely land.

Single-engine planes aren't meant to be flown in instrument weather, but knowing the full professional ways—with GCA, ILS and the best instrument methods—makes flying far safer for you, and a lot more fun, in that you've built your skill to an even finer point.

Chapter Sixteen. THE WEEKEND BIRDMEN, OR WHERE DO WE GO FROM HERE?

Saturday mornings, while most of the nation is still recuperating from the past week's work, thousands of engines roar into life at hundreds of airfields across the United States and a bewildering collection of brightly-painted small planes sweep off into the early morning light. The weekend birdmen (our winged confreres) are off again, headed anywhere from Mexico to Mackinac Island (in northern Michigan), or to Martha's Vineyard (on Cape Cod), on one of the zaniest, most challenging forty-eight-hour junkets conceivable.

Dedicated to the proposition that flying is the best possible escape from their hypertense or humdrum weekday routine, the birdmen count scientists, doctors, auctioneers, lawyers, writers, musicians, plumbers, carpenters and even housewives in their ranks. They're a special breed of urbanite or suburbanite who have found in flying a three-dimensional escape requiring unique skills—navigation, meteorology and airmanship—unused in office or home.

A major force behind the nation's current flying boom, the weekend pilots are out for fun and adventure and find widely varying quantities of both. They shun the antics of sports car devotees, sometimes stoop to boating, but are seldom happy unless an airplane engine, preferably the engine of *their* plane, is cranking over smoothly and then are outward bound on a trip to a newly discovered resort or vacation spot.

Upwards of 150,000 weekend fliers, from 17 to 70, man nearly 100,000 planes, including aged Piper Cubs and Aeronca Champs, swift new Comanches, Cessna 310s, Cherokee, Beech Musketeers and Debonairs. The older, used ships sell for as little as $1200, the new twin-engine jobs for as much as $95,000.

The typical weekend pilot owns, or more likely yearns for, one of the newer four-passenger tricycle-gear planes, such as the ubiquitous Tri-Pacer (the MG of the air age), a Cherokee, or the Cessna 172 or 175, which sell new for about $10,000 to $13,000 fully equipped and can be picked up a year or two old for $7000 to $10,000.

The weekend pilot will often start flying with a vintage plane, such as a 20-year-old Cub. It may look old, the paint is peeling disgracefully, and wide open it won't

"Now all we need is *one* plane for ourselves."

do any more than 90 mph, but it's as safe as any new aircraft, since the Federal Aviation Agency inspectors annually subject all private planes to rigorous engine and body inspections.

By the time his inspection rolls around, the weekend flier is so numbed from his other expenses that he can't, and seldom even tries, to talk the FAA man out of ordering him to replace whole sections of fabric. It would hardly pay, anyway, since FAA men are a bit like traffic cops: the harder you argue, the worse it goes for you.

So, after a game battle, the part-time pilot gallantly surrenders. Anyway, the repairs seem like mere cigaret money when stacked up against the other bills. Before he can get his private license (allowing him to take up family and friends), the weekend birdman will pay from $600 to $1000 for instruction, depending on the type of plane he uses. In a rented Cub or Champ, dual instruction is from $12 to $15 an hour; in a Tri-Pacer or Cessna 172, from $18 to $23. And if you're one of those fortunate enough to own your own plane the price to be paid to an instructor is from $4 to $6 an hour, plus the running expenses of your plane, which will be from $8 to $14 an hour depending on the plane. That much-heralded solo flight, as we now know, earns only the student license, entitling the student pilot to fly only himself and to build up his hours and skill.

A Comanche over Edgartown, Massachusetts.

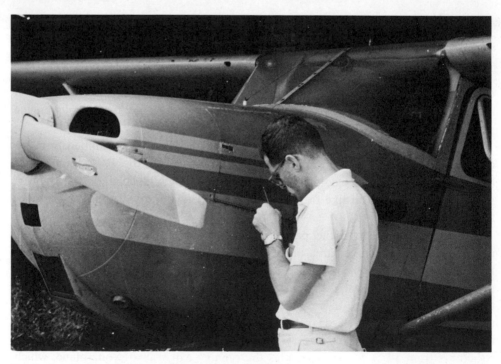

"Now, I wonder where *that* gizmo came from." Keith Connes, whose romance with the sky began six years and several thousand hours ago, has been known to desert home, office or even a good party, to get in an airplane – *any* airplane at *any* hour of the day or night. Connes' Cessna 180 has been all over the United States; with him flying has long ceased to be a weekend sport – it is a full-time passion.

After winning his wings, the weekend flier generally scoots out and buys a plane,
either alone or, often, with his closest friend, who then usually becomes an ex-
friend, since both invariably want to use the plane the same hours each weekend.
Solution: get a plane with a friend who works different hours, has days off during
the week, and takes his vacation when you can't, or doesn't like to fly.

With his newly acquired plane, the birdman blithely bids farewell to jammed
highways, tunnels and bridges, little realizing (and refusing to concede, anyway),
that he still must suffer the indignity of driving to and from the airport. In the air
itself is where time is saved.

Chicago birdmen find that Wisconsin's fabled Eagle River fishing country, a
rugged eight-hour road trip, is about two and a half hours away by plane.
Mackinac Island, the old-world resort between Upper and Lower Michigan, a day-
long nightmare by car, can be reached by plane from Chicago in less than four
hours. Many Windy City fliers do their pheasant shooting five hundred miles west-
ward in South Dakota—three hours in a Comanche, four to five hours in a Tri-
Pacer or Cessna 172. It is a practical weekend by plane, though almost impossible
by auto.

Fleeing the smog of Los Angeles, we birdmen can touch down in the clear
desert air of Palm Springs in less than an hour. Sky ranches, with their own airstrips, motels and swimming pools, are another popular target for us. Further south
lies the Baja California peninsula of Mexico, still far from cluttered civilization, but
now being opened up by air.

On short hops, however, weekend birdmen sometimes find that timesaving
schemes backfire. Montauk, on the tip of Long Island, famed for its deep-sea fishing, takes only forty-five minutes by plane from metropolitan New York. But the
entire trip may take longer to fly than to drive if the pilot gets hung up in road
traffic on his way to the airport. Another mounting problem: the traffic tieup at
the airport—of planes waiting for clearance to take off.

Fishermen find flying adds hours of sport and opens new fishing areas to them.

It isn't long before we weekend birdmen brag about time savings only to ourselves and our fellow pilots. We tell sports car friends that we fly for the love of flying, which is the plain unvarnished truth. There are fewer arguments that way. Some weekend destinations are easily accessible by a commercial airline, a horrifying thought to private pilots, who would never dream of going in any conveyance but their own plane. Not only is this more satisfying, but (weather allowing), they can then arrive and leave when they want to.

Searching for choice locales far away from big cities, uncrowded and inexpensive, we weekend pilots often belatedly discover we have stretched our wings too far, and are marooned by bad weather. Uniquely talented members of the species manage to get grounded by snow, clouds, thunderstorms or fog at a place from which there is absolutely no chance of getting back to work by Monday. Employers have been known to be unwilling to believe anybody could be stuck in Iron Mountain, Michigan, Myrtle Beach, South Carolina, or some equally unlikely locale.

After a while, bosses either get conditioned to apologetic Monday morning phone calls, or birdmen find that they are full-time fliers. One former Madison

Kaya Meredith drops off her husband, actor-director Burgess Meredith, for a performance. "On the road" to them means "In the air."

Avenue advertising man, now in California, found himself fogbound several days running at an ocean resort and in bad with the boss. Thinking furiously, he "brainstormed" his way out of trouble by cultivating several new clients for his agency. He even flew them back after the fog lifted, much to the delight of the agency chief, and they promptly signed.

There are also, it must be pointed out, the disillusioned and embittered types in our ranks, whose bosses and wives refuse to believe us after the third or fourth time we get clipped by weather. Such bitter specimens are to be found sulking alone, at the corner of the local airport, social outcasts, muttering to themselves, "Go by air when you have time to spare."

If it isn't swimming, fishing, hunting or skiing season, the true birdman will go somewhere anyway "just to get in the air." Many, who took up flying to get away from their fellow men, turn out to be gregarious after all; they love nothing more than to gab for hours with fellow fliers. The species has also been known to fly ludicrous distances to free-load. When Piper Aircraft offered a buffet party some years ago to celebrate turning out its 45,000th plane, 750 aircraft from all over the nation swamped the field at Lock Haven, landing right over one another in all

It takes several big snowstorms before footprints instead of tire marks are the only identification for the taxiways at Ramapo Valley.

corners of the field. The control tower man quietly had a nervous breakdown and fled. There were numerous cases of shattered nerves, but not a single dented wing-tip. Joanne and I were there, we know, but still can't believe what we saw and experienced as we landed. At one point we watched eight planes lined up on final ready to land and another dozen or so in the pattern. An Allegheny Airlines pilot trying to make a scheduled landing with his twin-engine commercial transport took one look at the airborne confusion and promptly turned tail on the whole procedure. He radioed Lock Haven declaring that he wasn't going to land *his* airplane in that chaos, and headed for Williamsport.

Weather aside, the biggest enemy fliers encounter is the high cost of the hobby. Aviation gas is more than 40 cents a gallon in most states (the typical private plane burns 6 to 9 gallons an hour), though most states offer a tax refund of from 3 cents to 5 cents on the gallon. Hangaring is $25 to $50 a month. After totaling up these items, as well as maintenance, insurance and depreciation, the hourly operating cost can add up to as high as $10. Some birdmen have an insatiable hunger to roam and frequently may clock 300 hours a year. Annual cost: $3000. Most average a far lower amount, flying perhaps 100 hours yearly.

We pilots, sensitive to tales of the dangers we face, retort by claiming that the biggest risk is the car trip to and from the field. In the air, we point out, man is a far more frail—and suddenly more cautious—creature than on the ground. And, federal and local regulations aside, fliers follow the deeply personal law of self-preservation. The nation's 450,000 active private and business pilots flew nearly 120,000 planes on an average of more than 12,000,000 hours these past few years, and were involved in about 4000 accidents, many of which were no more than a bruised wingtip or strut. In each of those years motor vehicles figured in more than 10,000,000 accidents. Surprisingly, professional, military and airline pilots, rather than fearing weekend fliers as a menace to aviation, accept them as winged comrades in the air ocean, which is shared by all—private planes below, and the fast military jets and airline ships up higher, each on their own air lanes.

Compared to sports car aficionados or yachtsmen, we fliers are a sedate lot. We don't try to break speed records or compete against one another; flying is too individualistic a sport. Many of us fly to be free, alone and unfettered, reaching out to touch the spirit of infinity as we sail through a solitary sky. Some of us fly for the visual poetry close to great banks and mountains of multihued clouds. Still others of us lose our weekday worries in the concentrated art, coordination and exhilaration of being airborne at the controls, dancing an aerodynamic ballet on an incomparable stage. And to still another group, flying is just a swifter way of getting from A to B. All of us share the same passion for the act of being airborne—the instant freedom of feeling our plane pull itself off the ground.

It is a passion many of us are unable to confine. A window-washing entrepreneur and flier, arriving to work at our home in the country one day not long ago, saw the clouds lifting through the grime of the unwashed picture window, and fled excitedly, declaring, "I've *got* to fly." He hightailed it to the local airport, leaving ladders, buckets and other gear in the driveway.

The flying passion has smitten a goodly number of our wives, who choose to become weekend copilots instead of weekend widows, and who now fly alongside their husbands. Some go on their own. One birdgirl, after getting her license,

Your friends are only hours, not days, away.

One Zero Zulu at Greenwood Lake Airport in New Jersey, a new field right off the corner
of the resort lake, which is being developed as the airstrip for an industrial park.

sneaked out of the house early on a Sunday while her husband still slept. She ran out of gas and her engine quit, fortunately within gliding range of a Strategic Air Command base, where she landed, violating all manner of regulations, since Air Force bases are prohibited to private planes.

Surrounded by angry Air Force personnel, she discovered that she'd forgotten her license, logbook or any form of identification. To back up her story, she insisted that her husband be called. Awakened from a sound sleep, the poor fellow was asked if he knew where his wife was. "Sure," he answered drowsily, "right in the next bed sleeping," and he groggily hung up without looking. It took another phone call and the beseeching voice of his wife before the husband turned over and discovered his birdgirl had flown the coop.

The weekend birdmen and birdgirls are here to stay.

Taxiing toward the main runway at Ramapo Valley Airport, the controls suddenly felt sluggish and unresponsive when I started to turn a corner. In the co-pilot's seat, six-year-old David's hands were locked around the wheel and he swiveled it back and forth like a racing driver at Indianapolis. He was steering one way, *his* way.

"All right, already," I chided him. "Let go of the wheel."

"Hey you," he shot back, *"I'm* flying this plane."

It was pretty ridiculous since he was still too small to even see over the windshield, but he'd solved that problem by looking up; his eyes were fixed on the sky. He was flying the Cherokee.

Two of Spring Valley's devout birdgirls, Julie Van Saal (on the left), and Kaya Meredith, wife of actor-director Burgess Meredith, check out their maps in the Comanche. Both are accomplished pilots, with their instrument ratings, and pilot their own ships – Cessna 182 Skylanes.

Now that we both have our licenses, David's major problem in life has been solved and he can go around bragging to his playmates, "My mommy got her license. Now she can take me up." If he never flies a plane as an adult, David has already had several careers of piloting, mentally handling virtually every ship that he's seen on any of the dozens of airports he's landed at and visited. Simple— at age four!

"What do you want to be when you grow up?"

"A pilot, you silly-billy."

"But what kind of pilot?"

"Uh . . . American jet pilot." (That meant a commercial jet.)

Or . . .

"Uh . . . a contrail jet." (That denoted a military jet.)

Or . . .

"Uh . . . a *funny* plane." (And this, of course, was a biplane.)

Or . . .

"Uh . . . daddy plane." (Naturally, this was the Tri-Pacer.)

Or . . .

"Uh . . . an S-15 to outer space." (The X-15.)

Or . . .

"Lemme see . . . a moon doctor." (This somehow means a space medic on a rocket ship.)

Or . . . lately:

"First, we gotta get mommy a plane of her own . . . a little one for Beth . . . and then I'll get a big one like you. . . ." By the time he's ten, we'll have an air force of our own.

All of the foregoing can only be taken to mean that youngsters are now growing up in a world where a car may someday seem as strange as an airplane. And even if the airplane is still just a trifle unusual, it is fast becoming commonplace. It is just as rapidly opening a new world of adventure and vacation possibilities to hundreds of thousands of fliers and their families.

One of the reasons we'd taken up flying in the first place was because we were both sick of cars, clogged highways and the crass commercialism of the American road. In the plane, we could go farther in less time, seek out vacation hideaways inaccessible on four wheels, and have ourselves fun flying there.

We've already explored New England, the Atlantic Coast and some of the Midwest via small airplane. Target for tomorrow: the national parks in the Far West, Alaska and, ultimately, an extended hop around South America.

Whether you like such long hops, or get just as much of a kick out of flying two hundred miles in an hour and thirty minutes to visit friends or relatives, the family airplane offers a challenging new way to get there. For many, including us, there doesn't even have to be a place to go; many a pleasant afternoon has been spent just going up for an hour or so as a break in the routine after a rugged day; many fine summer days have developed out of thirty-minute hops to a lake or beach in the mountains or on the Jersey shore.

As for children, even of the real small variety, airplanes seem to have a marvelous effect. For fifteen minutes they're interested in everything and then, in about four seconds flat, they're asleep, lulled by the steady droning of the engine.

Flying has become a family affair, as the Bergmans show how it's done.

They generally stay knocked out for a good hour or two; we've discovered that the family plane can be a much better setting for talking to each other than the family living room. Try and figure out a way to get the kids asleep in the house and you'll know what we mean.

One of the big spurs behind our flying boom is the dual use lots of us are getting out of airplanes, using them during the week for business hops; then, on weekends, rediscovering the plane as a shortcut to leisure pleasure. Everybody from doctors to farmers, salesmen and psychiatrists (fed up, naturally, with listening to the complaints of others) have discovered the solace, speed and satisfaction to be found in the cabin of a comfortable four-place airplane. And those who use the plane for business can also pay off part of the expense in tax deductions.

With the many thousands of airports spanning the United States, the airways are becoming as heavily loaded with traffic as the turnpikes. The difference is that the road jams seldom get solved; the traffic jam in the skies, which develops at odd times, is already the subject of comprehensive studies by the FAA. The flying boom now sweeping the United States seems to be getting bigger and stronger each year.

Scores of new airports are opening in vacation areas; it's possible to land in many parks and alongside many of the major American lakes; dude ranches, hotels, health resorts and even some gambling joints have their own airstrips. Many of the newer spots have their runways so close to the pools, restaurants and recreation areas that it's no longer necessary to rent a car when you land. Some of the newest fliers' nests in the Southwest are laid out so that you can taxi-up almost to your motel quarters.

And even when you aren't filling out a vacation, there's always a crowd (though sometimes a small one) at almost any airport, anxious to trade tales about airplanes and other high-spirited creatures of mutual interest. The air age has even given rise to a newly-cloaked, if familiar, sociological phenomenon, the air bum. Like the now-familiar beach bum, the species turns up anywhere and everywhere, following the seasons around to airports in the proper climate, from West Palm Beach north to Nantucket and west to Santa Monica. None of them ever seem to work much, but always have enough cash on hand to stake themselves to an hour's rental of a plane just in case no one wants cockpit company when they need a spell of flying.

The mark of the breed is generally the crumpled leather World War II Air Corps flying jacket. Since there couldn't have been that many jackets issued during or after the war, somebody must have quite a business going in precrumpled, properly aged flying jackets.

A counterpoint to the air bums is supplied by the status-seekers of aviation who, just like their counterparts in boating, shooting or what-have-you, are always one step ahead in the latest bit of flying gear, the newest piece of navigational gear, and either the newest but worst-kept airplane, or the oldest but best-kept airplane.

But just get a good fly-in going to a choice lake, island airport, or beach, and the social barriers crumble in the few minutes it takes to check the weather. People who wouldn't speak to each other on the street are lifelong companions, united by the individually sacred love of being airborne that is the driving force behind the American Air Age.

Now, if we could only really afford one airplane, much less two planes and a little one as well . . .

We'll be right there. . . . And so we hope, will you.

"I'm sorry, this is all we have left for you to rent this weekend." (*Replica of Clyde Cessna's 1911 monoplane. Powered with a 6-cylinder radial engine rated at 50 to 60 hp, it flew at a top speed of 50 mph.*)

PICTURE GALLERY
AMERICA'S USED
PRIVATE AIRCRAFT

While almost everybody wants to own a new airplane, sometimes it's impossible —you may just not have or want to put that kind of money into a plane. Many student pilots buy themselves a good used plane for prices ranging from $1500 to $5000, in order to learn to fly in it, and thus avoid the hazard of banging up a brand-new ship. Then, after learning, they buy a new plane.

Many others stick to the used plane, finding that it fulfills their flying needs and holds down their investment. Actually, it's hard to find a sounder investment than a used plane, if it has been and is kept in good shape. There's so great a demand for some types of used planes that are no longer available that they hold their value with almost no depreciation. Some fliers, in fact, have had the rare experience of buying a used Cub, for example, for $2000, learning to fly in it, and then selling it for prices up to $2500.

On the pages that follow are a gallery of the most popular of the private planes in use across the country. Some are faster and more powerful than many of the new ships being turned out. Most are far slower, far less powerful, consume much less gasoline and cost much less than the brand-new ships.

The familiar ERCOUPE, one of the first all-metal tricycle-gear airplanes manufactured, is now reappearing as a new plane. Its makers went out of the business of making ERCOUPES only to find later that a demand still existed. The city of Carlsbad, New Mexico, searching for an industry for itself, went into the airplane-making business in a unique deal that has resulted in new ERCOUPES and a good industry for a city.

First turned out with a 65 hp engine, later ERCOUPES with modifications got up to 75 hp. The two-passenger ship, with a bubble canopy, has terrific cockpit visibility, flies at a top speed of about 100 mph. An ERCOUPE in good condition sells for between $2000 and $2500.

The BELLANCA, which first was produced twenty years ago, is now being made in modern form. The BELLANCA first appeared as the CRUISAIR (as illustrated) with conventional gear and a 150 hp engine. Later versions offered a 165 hp engine. Still later, the CRUISEMASTER version, with a husky 190 hp motor, appeared. BELLANCAS cruise at about 140 mph. The CRUISAIR sells for around $3800; the CRUISEMASTER, with tricycle gear and more power, for up to $6000. Both are four-seat airplanes.

CESSNA's classic 140, another of the early all-metal ships, appeared right after World War II. First models had a fabric wing; later versions, all metal, were designated the 140A. The 140 series had 85 and 90 hp engines, cruised at 110–115 mph, and carried two persons side by side. In good shape, the airplane sells for around $2700.

The TAYLORCRAFT. Not many of them are seen any more. The original T-CRAFT was one of the United States' first practical private planes and it led to development of the PIPER series of planes. There were at least four different basic TAYLORCRAFT models; most appeared with 65 hp engines, carried two persons side by side, and had a top cruising speed of 90 mph. With its big wing, the T-CRAFT was soon dubbed "the floater." The pilot had to work to get the plane on the ground where he wanted it – they loved to float right on down the runway.

The NAVION, first made by North American Aviation, later by Ryan, and now being turned out again after being out of production for years. Still one of the most beautiful planes in the United States. The NAVION was a fast plane when it came out not long after the Second World War. It carried four persons at speeds to 135 mph and had a well-founded reputation as a rugged piece of hardware. Its all metal frame and wings could take plenty of beating. The NAVION was turned out in 205 hp, 225 hp and finally in 265 hp versions. The plane, many claimed, burned more gas than comparable ships, such as the BONANZA, and cost more for upkeep, but it held onto its popularity. Price range – $6000–7500 – depending, as all planes do, on how many radios it has and how good they are.

The AERONCA CHIEF, another of the early United States' side-by-side planes. Now out of production, the CHIEF is still a sought-after ship. It carries two persons side by side, cruises at about 80 mph, and is powered by a 65 hp engine in most models. CHIEFS sell in the $1300–1400 price bracket.

The AERONCA CHAMP, one of the United States' classic trainers, is still in demand by airport operators. Like the original J-3 PIPER CUBS, CHAMPS never seem to wear out. It appeared in 65 hp and 85 hp versions, and cruised at 80 mph; CHAMPS sell for about $1300.

The Luscombe Silvaire, which was built primarily as a landplane. Two Silvaire models appeared, the 8A and the 8E. The 8A had a 65 hp engine and cruised at 85 mph; the 8E, powered by 85 and 90 hp engines, got up to 110 mph. Both are two-place ships. 8A's sell for about $1700; 8E's go for about $2300.

The Luscombe Silvaire float-equipped.

Another of the popular AERONCA series – the SEDAN. A husky four-seater, the SEDAN is powered by a 125 hp engine and cruises in the vicinity of 95 mph. Price: $2300.

The STINSON VOYAGER, which appeared in both fabric and metal versions. The original version, the 108, had 150 hp and cruised above 120 mph; the later version, the 150, had 165 hp and cruised just above 125 mph. Price range: fabric version – $3000; the all-metal version – $4500.

The PIPER SUPER-CRUISER, blood brother of the classic J-3 CUB. Powered with engines up to 100 hp, the Super-Cruiser carried three persons (one in front, two in back), cruised at 100–105 mph and boasted a six-hour flying range. It sold new, in 1946, for $2905. A good SUPER-CRUISER is now worth about $2100, which is remarkable proof of how airplanes can hold their value.

The PIPER TRI-PACER, out of production after eleven years. More than 7000 TRI-PACERS, ranging from 135 hp to 160 hp, were manufactured and the aircraft dominated the tricycle-gear market after pioneering in it. Prices range anywhere from $3000 for an older, worn model to $7500 for recent versions. Produced by PIPER only in fabric form, hundreds of TRI-PACERS have been metallized and will last for years in the popular plane market.

PICTURE GALLERY
AMERICA'S PRIVATE AND
BUSINESS PLANES

Priced from $5000 up through $150,000, United States private and business planes offer an amazing range of types and a great diversity of accessories. They go all the way from the two-place Super Cub and Cessna 150 through eight-passenger executive planes.

All offer good flight safety and every one of them flies well; it's a matter of picking what you want, and how much you can afford to pay. Specific prices, which have a habit of changing rapidly, are not mentioned; they can be checked easily enough at any airport or with any dealer. All of the planes can be test-flown by arranging it with a dealer, and many can be rented for several hours or a day, if you get serious about buying one and really want to get used to it to see if it is the plane for you.

PIPER COLT. Two-place, fabric, fixed tricycle-gear landplane.

SPECIFICATIONS

Engine	Lycoming O-235-CIB
Horsepower and rpm	108 @ 2600
Gross weight (lb.)	1650
Empty weight (standard – lb.)	940
Empty weight (Super Custom – lb.)	985
Useful load (standard – lb.)	710
Useful load (Super Custom – lb.)	665
Wing span (ft.)	30
Wing area (sq. ft.)	147
Length (ft.)	20
Height (ft.)	6.25
Power loading (lb. per hp)	15.3
Wing loading (lb. per sq. ft.)	11.2
Baggage capacity (lb.)	100
Fuel capacity (standard – gal.)	18
Fuel capacity (optional – gal.)	36

PERFORMANCE

Top speed (mph)	120
Cruising speed (75% power, mph at sea level)	108
Optimum cruising speed (75% power, mph at 7000 ft.)	115
Stalling speed (mph)	54
Takeoff run (ft.)	950
Takeoff over 50 ft. barrier (ft.)	1500
Landing roll (ft.)	500
Landing distance (over 50 ft. barrier – ft.)	1250
Best rate-of-climb speed (mph)	75
Rate of climb (ft. per min., sea level)	610
Best angle-of-climb speed (mph)	60
Service ceiling (ft.)	12,000
Absolute ceiling (ft.)	14,400
Fuel consumption (gal. per hr. 75% power, leaned)	6
Cruising range (standard fuel, 75% power, SL)	3 hr., 324 mi.
Cruising range (standard fuel, 75% power, 7000 ft.)	3 hr., 345 mi.
Cruising range (opt. fuel, 75% power, SL)	6 hr., 648 mi.
Cruising range (opt. fuel, 75% power, 7000 ft.)	6 hr., 690 mi.

PIPER CHEROKEE. Four-place, all-metal, fixed tricycle-gear landplane.

SPECIFICATIONS

	PA-28-150	PA-28-160	PA-28-180	PA-28-235
Engine	Lycoming	Lycoming	Lycoming	Lycoming
Hp and rpm	150 @ 2700	160 @ 2700	180 @ 2700	235 @ 2900
Gross weight (lb.)	2150	2200	2400	2900
Empty weight (std.) (lb.)	1205	1210	1225	1410
Useful load (std.) (lb.)	945	990	1175	1490
Empty weight				
(AutoFlite model) (lb.)	1245	1250	1265	1470
Useful load (AutoFlite model) (lb.)	905	950	1135	1430
Wing span (ft.)	30	30	30	32.0
Wing area (sq. ft.)	160	160	160	170
Length (ft.)	23.3	23.3	23.3	23.5
Height (ft.)	7.3	7.3	7.3	7.1
Power loading (lb. per hp)	14.3	13.8	13.3	12.4
Wing loading (lb. per sq. ft.)	13.4	13.8	15.0	17.0
Baggage capacity (lb.)	125	125	125	200
Fuel capacity, (standard, gal.)	36*	36*	50*	84

* 50 gals. with built-in reserve

PERFORMANCE

	PA-28-150	PA-28-160	PA-28-180	PA-28-235
Top speed (mph)	139 (142**)	141 (144**)	150	166
Optimum cruising speed				
(75% power, mph at 7000 ft.)	130 (133**)	132 (135**)	141	156
Stalling speed (flaps down, mph)	53	55	57	60
Takeoff run (ft.)	800	775	775	800
Landing roll (flaps down, ft.)	535	550	600	680
Best rate-of-climb speed (mph)	85	85	85	100
Rate of climb (ft. per min.)	660	700	720	825
Service ceiling (ft.)	14,300	15,000	15,000	14,500
Absolute ceiling (ft.)	16,800	17,500	18,300	16,500
Fuel consumption				
(gal. per hr., 75% power)	9	9	10	14
Cruising range				
(75% power, optimum				
altitude, mi.)	715*	725*	695	935
Optimum cruising range				
(55% power, optimum				
altitude, mi.)	790*	805*	750	1130

* with reserve fuel
** with optional speed fairings

PIPER COMANCHE 180 AND 250. Four-place, all-metal, retractable tricycle-gear landplane.

SPECIFICATIONS

	PA-24 "180"	PA-24 "250"
Engine	Lycoming O-360-A	Lycoming O-540-A1A5
Hp and rpm	180 @ 2700	250 @ 2575
Gross weight (lb.)	2550	2900
Empty weight (lb.)	1530	1690
Useful load (lb.)	1020	1210
Wing span (ft.)	36	36
Wing area (sq. ft.)	178	178
Length (ft.)	24.7	24.9
Height (ft.)	7.3	7.3
Power loading (lb. per hp)	14.2	11.2
Wing loading (lb. per sq. ft.)	14.3	15.7
Baggage capacity (lb.)	200	200
Fuel capacity (standard, gal.)	50	60
Fuel capacity (with reserve fuel, gal.)	60	90

PERFORMANCE

	PA-24 "180"	PA-24 "250"
Top speed (mph)	167	190
Optimum cruising speed (75% power, opt. alt., mph)	160	181
Stalling speed (flaps down, mph)	61	61
Takeoff run (ft.)	750	760
Landing roll (flaps down, ft.)	600	650
Best rate-of-climb speed (mph)	96	95
Rate of climb (fpm)	910	1350
Service ceiling (ft.)	18,500	20,000
Absolute ceiling (ft.)	21,000	22,000
Fuel consumption (75% power, gal. per hr.)	10	14
Cruising range (75% power, sea level, standard fuel)	5 hr. 750 mi.	4.3 hr. 740 mi.
Cruising range, optimum (standard fuel)	6.2 hr. 920 mi.	7.5 hr. 1100 mi.
Cruising range (75% power, sea level, reserve fuel)	6 hr. 900 mi.	6.4 hr. 1100 mi.
Cruising range, optimum (reserve fuel)	7.5 hr. 1100 mi.	11.2 hr. 1650 mi.

PIPER TWIN COMANCHE. Four-place, twin-engine, all-metal, retractable tricycle-gear landplane.

SPECIFICATIONS

Model	PA-30
Engine	IO-320-B
Hp and rpm	160 at 2700
Gross weight (lb.)	3600
Empty weight (standard model) (lb.)	2160
Useful load (standard) (lb.)	1440
Wing span (ft.)	36
Wing area (sq. ft.)	178
Propeller diameter (in.)	72
Length (ft.)	25.1
Height (ft.)	7.3
Power loading (lb. per hp)	11.25
Wing loading (lb. per sq. ft.)	20.22
Baggage capacity (lb.)	200
Baggage space (cu. ft.)	20
Fuel capacity (gal.)	90*
Wheel base (ft.)	7.3
Wheel tread (ft.)	9.8
	*84 gal. usable

PERFORMANCE

Top speed (mph)	205
Cruising speed (75% power at sea level, mph)	181
Optimum cruising speed (75% power at 8000 ft., mph)	194
Cruising speed (65% power at 12,000 ft., mph)	186
Stall speed (power off, flaps ext., mph)	69
Takeoff run at sea level (ft.)	950
Takeoff distance over 50 ft. at sea level (ft.)	1570
Landing roll at sea level (ft.)	1215
Landing over 50 ft. at sea level (ft.)	1875
Best rate-of-climb speed at sea level (mph)	112
Rate of climb at sea level (ft. per min.)	1460
Best angle-of-climb speed (mph)	90
Best single-engine rate-of-climb speed (sea level, mph)	105
Single engine rate of climb at sea level (ft. per min.)	260
Absolute ceiling (ft.)	20,000
Service ceiling (ft.)	18,600
Single-engine absolute ceiling (ft.)	7100
Single-engine service ceiling (ft.)	5800
Fuel consumption (65% power, gal. per hr.)	17.2
Fuel consumption (75% power, gal. per hr.)	15.2
Cruising range – max. (75% power at 8000 ft., mi.)	948
Cruising range – max. (65% power at 12,000 ft., mi.)	1025

PIPER APACHE. Four- or five-place, twin-engine, all-metal, retractable gear landplane.

SPECIFICATIONS

Gross weight (lb.)	4800	4400
Engine	Lycoming	Lycoming
	O-540-B1A5	O-540-B1A5
	235 hp. 2575 rpm	235 hp, 2575 rpm
Empty weight (standard, lb.)	2735	2735
Useful load (standard, lb.)	2065	1665
Empty weight (AutoFlite, lb.)	2850	2850
Useful load (AutoFlite, lb.)	1950	1550
Fuel capacity (gal.)	144	144
Wing span (ft.)	37	37
Wing area (sq. ft.)	207	207
Length (ft.)	27.6	27.6
Height (ft.)	10.3	10.3
Wing loading (lb. per sq. ft.)	23.2	21.3
Power loading (lb. per hp)	10.2	9.36
Baggage capacity (lb. maximum)	200	200
Baggage compartment space (cu. ft.)	25	25
Cargo space, (cu. ft.)		
rear seat removed	80	80

PERFORMANCE

Top speed (mph)	202	204
Cruising speed at altitude		
(7000 ft. at 75% power, mph)	191	195
Stalling speed (power off, flaps down, mph)	62	59
Takeoff run (ft., 25° flaps)	830	680
Landing roll (flaps down, ft.)	880	800
Best rate-of-climb speed (mph)	112	111
Rate of climb (fpm)	1450	1680
Best single-engine rate-of-climb speed (mph)	110	109
Single-engine rate of climb (fpm)	220	320
Service ceiling (ft.)	17,200	18,400
Absolute ceiling (ft.)	18,500	19,500
Single-engine absolute ceiling (ft.)	6600	8300
Fuel consumption (at 75% power, gal. per hr.)	28	28
Cruising range (at 75% power at 7000 ft., mi.)	1185	1245

Since most flights will not need the large payload designed into the Apache, performance and specifications at 4400 lb. gross are furnished as well as at 4800 lb.

PIPER AZTEC B. Four- to five-place, twin engine, all metal, retractable gear landplane.

SPECIFICATIONS

Engine	Two Lycoming O-540
Hp and rpm	250 @ 2575
Gross weight (lb.)	4800
Empty weight (standard, lb.)	2900
Useful load (standard, lb.)	1000
Empty weight (AutoFlite, lb.)	2990
Useful load (AutoFlite, lb.)	1810
Wing span (ft.)	37
Wing area (sq. ft.)	207
Length (ft.)	30.1
Height (ft.)	10.3
Power loading (lb. per hp)	9.6
Wing loading (lb. per sq. ft.)	23.5
Baggage capacity (lb.)	300
Baggage compartment space (cu. ft.)	38
Fuel capacity (gal.)	144

PERFORMANCE

Top speed (mph)	215
Optimum cruising speed (75% power at 7000 ft., mph)	205
Cruising speed (65% power at 10,000 ft., mph)	200
Stalling speed (mph)	62
Takeoff run (ft.)	750
Takeoff run over 50 ft. barrier (ft.)	1100
Landing roll (ft.)	900
Landing over 50 ft. barrier (ft.)	1260
Rate of climb (ft. per min.)	1650
Best rate-of-climb speed (mph)	112
Single-engine rate of climb (ft. per min.)	350
Best single-engine rate-of-climb speed (mph)	110
Absolute ceiling (ft.)	22,500
Service ceiling (ft.)	21,000
Single-engine absolute ceiling (ft.)	8800
Single-engine service ceiling (ft.)	7400
Fuel consumption (gal. per hr. at 75% power)	28
Fuel consumption (gal. per hr. at 65% power)	24
Cruising range (max. at 75% power at 7000 ft., mi.)	1025
Cruising range (max. at 65% power at 10,000 ft., mi.)	1200
Cruising range (max. at 45% power at 10,000 ft., mi.)	1400

BEECHCRAFT MUSKETEER. Four-place, all metal, fixed tricycle-gear land-plane.

SPECIFICATIONS

Gross weight, normal category	2300 lb.
Empty weight, with standard equipment	1300 lb.
Useful load, normal category	1000 lb.
Wing area	145.00 sq. ft.
Wing loading at gross weight	15.86 lb. per sq. ft.
Power loading at gross weight	14.38 lb. per hp
Baggage	140 lb.
Wing span	32 ft. 9 in.
Length	25 ft. 0 in.
Height	8 ft. 3 in.
Fuel capacity (30 gal. ea. tank)	60 gal. (58.8 gal. usable)
Fuel capacity (20 gal. ea. tank)	40 gal. (38.8 gal. usable)
Oil capacity – 8 qt.	6.0 qt. usable

PERFORMANCE

Maximum speed at 2700 rpm at sea level	144 mph
Cruising speeds	
At 75% power at 7000 ft.	135 mph
At 65% power at 10,000 ft.	127 mph
At 55 % power at 10,000 ft.	115 mph
Stall speed (power off, 30° flaps)	62 mph
Range	
At 75% power at 7,000 ft.	792 mi. on 60 gal.
	493 mi. on 40 gal.
At 65% power at 10,000 ft.	855 mi. on 60 gal.
	529 mi. on 40 gal.
At 55% power at 10,000 ft.	899 mi. on 60 gal.
	556 mi. on 40 gal.
Rate of climb at sea level (full throttle, gross weight)	710 fpm
Service ceiling	13,500 ft.
Absolute ceiling	15,600 ft.
Takeoff distance	
(at sea level, zero wind, standard temperature)	
Ground run	890 ft.
Total over 50 ft. obstacle	1320 ft.
Landing distance	
(at sea level, zero wind, standard temperature)	
Ground run	595 ft.
Total over 50 ft. obstacle	1215 ft.

BEECHCRAFT. Model 33 Debonair. Four-place, all-metal plane, with fully retractable tricycle landing gear.

SPECIFICATIONS

Engine	Continental 6-cylinder
Horsepower	225 @ 2600
Gross weight	3000 lb.
Empty weight	1745 lb.
Useful load	1255 lb.
Available weight for people, baggage and optional equipment with standard tanks full	933 lb.
Wing area	177.6 sq. ft.
Wing loading, at gross weight	16.9 lb. per sq. ft.
Power loading, at gross weight	13.3 lb. per hp
Wing span	32 ft. 10 in.
Length	25 ft. 6 in.
Height	8 ft. 3 in.
Fuel capacity, standard tanks (25 gal. ea.)	50 gal. (1 gal. unusable)
Fuel capacity, auxiliary tanks (10 gal. ea.)	20 gal. (1 gal. unusable)
TOTAL	70 gal. (2 gal. unusable)
Oil capacity	10 qt.

PERFORMANCE

Cruising speed (at 75% power (2450 rpm) at 7000 ft.)	185 mph
Range (at 50% power (154 mph) at 10,000 ft.)	840 mi. on 49 gal.
	1160 mi. on 68 gal.
Rate of climb at sea level (rated power, 225 hp)	960 fpm
Service ceiling	18,400 ft.
Absolute ceiling	20,500 ft.
Stalling speed (power off)	
Gear and flaps down 30°	60 mph
Gear and flaps up	71 mph
Takeoff distance	
(20° flaps, at sea level, zero wind, standard temperature)	
Ground run	940 ft.
Total over 50 ft. obstacle	1235 ft.
Landing distance	
(30° flaps, at sea level, zero wind, standard temperature)	
Ground run	635 ft.
Over 50 ft. obstacle	1282 ft.

BEECHCRAFT. Model 35 Bonanza. Four-place, all-metal, low-wing monoplane, with fully retractable tricycle landing gear.

SPECIFICATIONS

Engine	Continental 6-cylinder
Horsepower	260 @ 2625
	Standard
Maximum gross weight	3125 lb.
Standard empty weight	1855 lb.
Useful load	1270 lb.
Available weight for people, baggage and optional equipment with standard tanks full	948 lb.
Wing area	181.0 sq. ft.
Wing loading, at gross weight	17.3 lb. per sq. ft.
Power loading, at gross weight	12.0 lb. per hp
Wing span	33 ft. 5½ in.
Length	25 ft. 2 in.
Height	6 ft. 6½ in.
Fuel capacity, 50 gal. std. tanks (25 gal. ea.)	49 gal. usable
Fuel capacity, 79.5 gal. opt. tanks (39.75 gal. ea.)	78 gal. usable
Oil capacity	10 qt.

PERFORMANCE

Cruising speed (at 75% power (2450 rpm) at 7000 ft.)	195 mph
Range (at 75% power at 7000 feet)	540 mi. on 49 gal.
	960 mi. on 78 gal.
Rate of climb at sea level (rated power, 260 hp)	1150 fpm
Service ceiling	19,200 ft.
Absolute ceiling	21,000 ft.
Stall speed (power off)	
Gear and flaps down 30°	60 mph
Gear and flaps up	71 mph
Takeoff distance	
(20° flaps, at sea level, 10 mph wind, standard temperature)	
Ground run	745 ft.
Total over 50 ft. obstacle	1050 ft.
Landing distance	
(30° flaps, at sea level, 10 mph wind, standard temperature)	
Ground run	505 ft.
Total over 50 ft. obstacle	840 ft.

BEECHCRAFT. Model 95 Travel Air. Four- or five-place, all-metal, low-wing, twin-engine monoplane, with fully retractable tricycle landing gear.

SPECIFICATIONS

Engine	Two Lycoming 4-cylinder
Horsepower	180 @ 2700
Gross weight	4100 lb.
Empty weight	2635 lb.
Useful load weight	1465 lb.
Wing area	199.2 sq. ft.
Wing loading, at gross weight	20.6 lb. per sq. ft.
Power loading, at gross weight	11.4 lb. per hp
Baggage: Maximum 270 pounds – rear; 270 pounds less equipment – front	
Wing span	37 ft. 10 in.
Length	25 ft. 4 in.
Height	9 ft. 6 in.
Fuel: Main tanks (25 gal. ea.)	50 gal. (one gal. unusable)
Oil capacity (2 gal. ea. engine)	4 gal. (one gal. unusable)

PERFORMANCE

Cruising speed (75% power, 2450 rpm at 7500 ft.)	200 mph
High speed at sea level (2700 rpm, full throttle)	210 mph
Range (no reserve)	
65% power @ 195 mph	1160 mi. (112 gal.)
Maximum range @ 165 mph	1410 mi. (112 gal.)
Endurance	8.75 hr.
Rate of climb at sea level	1300 fpm
Service ceiling	18,700 ft.
Absolute ceiling	
Rated power at weight of	4100 lb.
Two engines	20,300 ft.
Stalling speed (zero thrust)	
Gear down, flaps 28°	70 mph
Takeoff distance	
At sea level, zero wind, standard temperature	1000 ft.
Total distance over 50 ft. obstacle	1280 ft.
Landing distance	
At sea level, zero wind, standard temperature	980 ft.
Total distance over 50 ft. obstacle	1590 ft.

BEECHCRAFT. Model 55 Baron. Four- or five-place, all-metal, low-wing mono-plane, with fully retractable tricycle landing gear.

SPECIFICATIONS

Engine	Two Continental 6-cylinder
Horsepower	260 @ 2625
Gross weight	4880 lb.
Empty weight	2960 lb.
Useful load	1920 lb.
Available weight for people and baggage with standard fuel tanks full	1191 lb.
Wing area	199.2 sq. ft.
Wing loading, at gross weight	24.5 lb. per sq. ft.
Power loading, at gross weight	9.4 lb. per hp
Baggage: Maximum 270 lb. – rear; 270 lb. less equipment – front	
Wing span	37 ft. 10 in.
Length	25 ft. 8 in.
Height	9 ft. 7 in.
Standard fuel arrangement (includes two main tanks, 25 gal. ea., and two auxiliary tanks, 31 gal. ea.)	112 gal.
Optional fuel arrangement (includes two main tanks, 39 gal. ea., and two auxiliary tanks, 31 gal. ea.)	140 gal.
Oil capacity	6 gal.

PERFORMANCE

Cruising speed (at 75% power, 2450 rpm, at 7000 ft.)	220 mph
High speed (at sea level 2625 rpm, full throttle)	230 mph
Range	1220 mi.
Rate of climb at sea level (rated power) Two engines at 4880 lb.	1630 fpm
Service ceiling (rated power) Two engines at 4880 lb.	19,200 ft.
Absolute ceiling Two engines at 4880 lb.	20,400 ft.
Stall speed (zero thrust), flaps 28°, gear down	76 mph
Takeoff distance (20° flaps) ground run	910 ft.
Total Distance over 50 ft. (at sea level, zero wind, standard temperature)	1255 ft.
Landing distance (28° flaps) ground run	1175 ft.
Total distance over 50 ft. (at sea level, zero wind, standard temperature)	1750 ft.

BEECHCRAFT. Model 50 Twin Bonanza. Six-place, all-metal, low-wing mono-plane, with retractable tricycle landing gear.

SPECIFICATIONS

Engine	Two Lycoming 6-cylinder
Horsepower	320 @ 3200
Gross weight	7300 lb.
Empty weight, dry	4470 lb.
Useful load	2830 lb.
Wing area	277.06 sq. ft.
Wing loading, at gross weight	26.4 lb. per sq. ft.
Power loading, at gross weight	11.4 lb. per hp
Baggage storage	Maximum 400 lb.
Wing span	45 ft. 11⅜ in.
Length	31 ft. 6½ in.
Height	11 ft. 4 in.
Fuel capacity, standard inboard tanks (44 gal. ea.)	88 gal.
Fuel capacity, standard outboard tanks (46 gal. ea.)	92 gal.
Oil capacity (4 gal. ea.)	8 gal.

PERFORMANCE

Performance	
Cruising speed	
70% power at 15,200 ft.	223 mph
70% power at 10,000 ft.	213 mph
65% power at 10,000 ft.	207 mph
High speed at 12,000 ft.	235 mph
Stalling speed – gear and flaps down	82.5 mph
Stalling speed – gear and flaps up	90 mph
Rate of climb at sea level	1270 fpm
Service ceiling	29,150 ft.
Absolute ceiling	30,600 ft.
Maximum range	*180 gal.*
65% power at 10,000 ft. (no reserve)	1095 mi.
45% power at 15,200 ft. (no reserve)	1295 mi.
Endurance	
65% power at 10,000 ft. (no reserve)	5.3 hr.
45% power at 10,000 ft. (no reserve)	7.2 hr.
Takeoff distance (with 20° flaps)	
Ground run	1110 ft.
Total over 50 ft. obstacle	1450 ft.
Landing over 50 ft. obstacle (full flaps)	
Landing weight	7000 lb.
Ground run	1000 lb.
Total over 50 ft. obstacle	1840 ft.

BEECHCRAFT. Model 65 Queen Air. Six- or eight-place, executive transport, all-metal, low-wing monoplane with retractable tricycle landing gear.

SPECIFICATIONS

Engine	Two Lycoming 6-cylinder
Horsepower	320 @ 3200
Gross weight	7700 lb.
Empty weight, dry	4660 lb.
Useful load	3040 lb.
Available weight for passengers, luggage and optional equipment with standard fuel tanks full	1924 lb.
Wing area	277.06 sq. ft.
Wing loading, at gross weight	27.8 lb. per sq. ft.
Power loading, at gross weight	12.03 lb. per hp
Baggage (with standard lavatory installation)	350 lb.
Wing span	45 ft. 10.5 in.
Length	33 ft. 4 in.
Fuel capacity, standard inboard tanks (44 gal. ea.)	88 gal.
Fuel capacity, standard outboard tanks (46 gal. ea.)	92 gal.
Oil capacity (4 gal. ea.)	8 gal. (2.9 gal. unusable)

PERFORMANCE

Cruising speeds	
At 70% mc power	
(2750 rpm) at 15,200 ft.	214 mph
(2750 rpm) at 10,000 ft.	205 mph
Cruising range	*180 gal.*
At 70% mc power at 15,200 ft.	760 mi.
at 10,000 ft.	760 mi.
at 5000 ft.	760 mi.
Maximum endurance (no reserve)	
At 35% mc power at 5000 ft.	8.5 hr.
Rate of climb at sea level – two engines	1300 fpm
Service ceiling – two engines (100 fpm)	31,300 ft.
Absolute ceiling – two engines	32,700 ft.
Stalling speed (zero thrust)	
Gear and flaps down 30°	80 mph
Gear and flaps up	94 mph
Takeoff distance – 20° flaps	
Ground run	1180 ft.
Total over 50 ft. obstacle	1560 ft.
Landing distance – 30° flaps	
Landing weight	7350 lb.
Ground run	1280 ft.
Total over 50 ft. obstacle	1685 ft.

BEECHCRAFT QUEEN AIR 80. Seven- or nine-place, all-metal, executive transport.

SPECIFICATIONS

Engine	Two Lycoming engines, 6-cylinder IGSO-540-A1A; supercharged; fuel injection
Horsepower	380 hp at 3400 rpm
Wing span	45 ft. 10.5 in.
Length	35 ft. 3 in.
Height to top of fin	14 ft. 8 in.
Baggage volume	29 cu. ft.
Capacity	350 lb.
Total fuel capacity (with optional auxiliary tanks)	230 gal.
Oil capacity	8 gal.

PERFORMANCE

High speed	252 mph
Normal cruising speed	230 mph
Two-engine rate of climb (at 7700 lb.)	1600 mph
Two-engine ceiling (at 6500 lb.)	35,700 ft.
Single-engine ceiling (at 6500 lb.)	21,500 ft.
Optimum range with fuel reserve (plus allowance for warm-up, taxi, takeoff and climb to altitude)	
Standard tanks	990 mi.
Extended range	1330 mi.
Stalling speed	77 mph

BEECHCRAFT SUPER H18. Eight-place executive transport.

SPECIFICATIONS

Gross weight	9900 lb.
Standard empty weight, dry	5680 lb.
Useful weight	4220 lb.
Area	360.7 sq. ft.
Wing loading, at gross weight	27.5 lb. per sq. ft.
Power loading, at gross weight	11 lb. per hp
Baggage (maximum baggage load)	300 lb.
Wing span	49 ft. 8 in.
Stabilizer span	15 ft.
Length	35 ft. 2½ in.
Fuel and oil capacity (standard tanks, 99 gal. ea.)	198 gal.
Oil capacity (7 gal. ea. engine)	14 gal.

PERFORMANCE

Cruising speeds (av. weight 8946 lb.)	
Using 300 hp per engine, 66% power	
(2000 rpm) at 10,000 ft.	220 mph
(2000 rpm) at 5000 ft.	290.5 mph
Using 200 hp per engine, 44.5% power	
(1800 rpm) at 10,000 ft.	185 mph
(1800 rpm) at 5000 ft.	178 mph
Maximum speeds	
At sea level	225 mph
At 4500 ft.	236 mph
At 10,000 ft.	235 mph
Cruising range	
200 hp, 5000 ft. (no wind)	1515 mi.
300 hp, 5000 ft.	1230 mi.
200 hp, 10,000 ft. (no wind)	1530 mi.
300 hp, 10,000 ft.	1260 mi.
Rate of climb (two engines at sea level)	1400 fpm
Service ceiling – two engines	20,800 ft.
Stalling speed – 0 Thrust and 0 Bank	
Gear and flaps down	87 mph
Gear and flaps up	93.5 mph
Takeoff distance to clear 50 ft. obstacle	2070 ft.
Landing distance to clear 50 ft. obstacle	1850 ft.

MOONEY MARK 21.   Four-seat, all-metal, retractable tricycle-gear landplane.

SPECIFICATIONS

Engine	Lycoming 4-cylinder, Model O-360
Horsepower	180
Gross weight	2575 lb.
Empty weight (approx.)	1525 lb.
Baggage	120 lb.
Wing loading, lb. per sq. ft.	15.4 lb.
Power loading, lb. per hp	14.3 lb.
Fuel capacity, total	48 gal.
Propeller	Mooney, metal, constant speed
Wing span	35 ft.
Wing area	167 sq. ft.
Height	8 ft. 4½ in.
Length	23 ft. 2 in.
Tread	9 ft. ¾ in.

PERFORMANCE

Speed	
Maximum at sea level	185 mph
Maximum cruising 75% power	180 mph
Normal cruising 69% power	171 mph
Economy cruising 62% power	159 mph
Range	
Normal range at 171 mph at 10,000 ft., no reserve	838 mi.
Maximum range at 122 mph at 10,000 ft., no reserve	952 mi.
Rate of climb, sea level	1010 fpm
Normal on-course climb at 120 mph, 2550 rpm	600 fpm
Service ceiling	17,200 ft.
Takeoff run, 0 mph wind, sea level	890 ft.
Landing run, 0 mph wind, sea level	550 ft.
Stall speed	57 mph

MOONEY MASTER. Four-seat, all-metal, fixed tricycle-gear landplane.

SPECIFICATIONS

Gross weight	2575 lb.
Empty weight	1475 lb.
Useful load	1100 lb.
Baggage	120 lb.
Wing loading	15.4 lb. per sq. ft.
Power loading	14.3 lb. per hp
Fuel capacity	48 gal.
Wing span	35 ft.
Wing area	167 sq. ft.
Tread	9 ft. ¾ in.
Length	23 ft. 2 in.

PERFORMANCE

Maximum speed	147 mph
Cruising speed	
75% power, 9600 ft., 2700 rpm	141 mph
75% power, 8000 ft., 2400 rpm	137 mph
65% power, 10,000 ft., 2400 rpm	130 mph
Stalling speed (2575 gross wt.)	57 mph
Rate of climb	
(sea level, flaps up, 92 mph, 2575 gross wt.)	780 fpm
Range	
Normal range 75% power, 8000 ft., 2400 rpm,	
no reserve	610 mi.
Maximum range 41% power, 10,000 ft., 1800 rpm	800 mi.
Service ceiling, 2575 gross wt., flaps up	12,000 ft.
Takeoff run, sea level, no wind, 2575 gross wt., 15° flaps	890 ft.
Landing roll, sea level, no wind, 2200 gross wt., 33° flaps	550 ft.

LAKE AMPHIBIAN. Four-place, all-metal amphibian.

SPECIFICATIONS

Engine	Direct cooled, 4-cylinder Ly-coming O-360-A1A
Horsepower	180 @ 2700
Gross weight	2400 lb.
Empty weight	1575 lb.
Useful load	825 lb.
Fuel capacity:	
Maximum	40 gal.
Normal	30 gal.
Minimum octane rating	91/96
Oil capacity	8 qt.
Power loading (lb. per hp)	13.3 lb.
Dimensions:	
Wing span	38 ft.
Wing area	170 sq. ft.
Wing loading (lb. per sq. ft.)	14.1 lb.
Length	24 ft. 11 in.
Height	9 ft. 4 in.

PERFORMANCE

Speed – standard air; gross weight:	
Normal cruising, 75% power at 6000 ft.	131 mph
Stalling speed	50 mph
Range – full fuel; gross weight:	
Maximum range	627 mi.
Normal cruising, 75% power at 6000 ft.	500 mi.
40 gal.	4 hr.
Rate of climb at sea level	800 fpm
Takeoff run, standard air; gross weight:	
Land	650 ft.
Water	1125 ft.
Landing roll – land	475 ft.
Landing run – water	600 ft.

BELLANCA 260. Four-seat, all-metal landplane.

SPECIFICATIONS

Gross weight	2700 lb.
Empty weight	1690 lb.
Useful load	1010 lb.
Wing span	34 ft. 2 in.
Fuselage length	22 ft. 11 in.
Wing loading	16.7 lb. per sq. ft.
Power loading	10.4 lb. per hp
Never exceed redline speed	226 mph

PERFORMANCE

Cruising speed, 75% at 9000 ft.	203 mph
Top speed	208 mph
Service ceiling	22,000 ft.
Absolute ceiling	26,500 ft.
Rate of climb	1750 fpm
Landing speed	49 mph
Takeoff distance	400 ft.
Landing roll	450 ft.
Range, maximum (60 gal. fuel, 65% power)	880 mi.
Range, normal (60 gal. fuel, 75% power)	770 mi.

HELIOCOURIER. Four- or five-place, all-metal landplane.

SPECIFICATIONS

	Courier Model H-395A	Super Courier Model H-395
Horsepower	260	295
Weight, empty (± 2%)	2020 lb.	2034 lb.
Gross, CAR* Part 3	3000 lb.	3000 lb.
Gross, CAR Part 8 (industrial uses only)	3920 lb.	3920 lb.
Useful load, CAR 3	980 lb.	963 lb.
Use load, CAR 8 (industrial uses only)	1900 lb.	1883 lb.
Dimensions: Length (3 pt.)	30 ft. 9 in.	30 ft. 9 in.
Height	8 ft. 10 in.	8 ft. 10 in.
Wing span	39 ft.	39 ft.

* Civil Air Rules affecting loads plane legally allowed to carry.

PERFORMANCE (all figures at zero wind)

Takeoff run	277 ft.	217 ft.
Takeoff distance over 50 ft. barrier	600 ft.	475 ft.
Landing roll with 40° commercial flap	169 ft.	169 ft.
Landing distance over 50 ft. barrier with 40° commercial flap	493 ft.	493 ft.
Minimum speed, power off	45 mph	45 mph
Minimum speed, power on (approx.)	30 mph	30 mph
Rate of climb	1250 ft. per min.	1350 ft. per min.
Service ceiling	20,050 ft.	22,500 ft.

CESSNA 150. Two-place, all-metal, fixed tricycle-gear landplane.

SPECIFICATIONS

Engine	Continental Engine O-200A
Horsepower	100 @ 2750
Baggage	80 lb.
Gross weight	1500 lb.
Empty weight (approx.)	950 lb.
Fuel capacity	26 gal.

PERFORMANCE

Top speed at sea level	127 mph
Cruising, 75% power at 7500 ft.	125 mph
Rate of climb at sea level	760 fpm
Range	
Cruising, 75% power at 7500 ft.	500 mi.
22.5 gal., no reserve	4.0 hr.
Optimum range at 10,000 ft.	610 mi.
22.5 gal., no reserve	5.9 hr.
Service ceiling	15,600 ft.

CESSNA 185 SKYWAGON. Four- or six-place, all-metal, fixed-gear landplane.

SPECIFICATIONS

Engine	Continental 6-cylinder, fuel injection IO-470-F
Horsepower	260 @ 2625
Baggage	350 lb.
Gross weight	3200 lb.
Empty weight (approx.)	1580 lb.
Fuel capacity (standard)	65 gal.
(optional)	84 gal.

PERFORMANCE

Top speed at sea level	176 mph
Cruising, 75% power at 7000 ft.	167 mph
Rate of climb at sea level	1000 fpm
Range	
Cruising, 75% power at 7000 ft.	730 mi.
62 gal., no reserve	4.4 hr.
Optimum range, at 10,000 ft.	1235 mi.
81 gal., no reserve	9.3 hr.
Service ceiling	17,300 ft.

CESSNA SKYMASTER. Twin-engine, all-metal, four- or six-place, fixed tricycle-gear landplane.

<h3 style="text-align:center">SPECIFICATIONS</h3>

Engine	Two Continental 6-cylinder, fuel injection IO-360-A
Horsepower	210 rated hp takeoff; 195 hp maximum continuous
Gross weight	3900 lb.
Empty weight (approx.)	2320 lb.
Baggage allowance	365 lb.
Fuel capacity: total (standard)	93 gal.
(optional)	131 gal.

<h3 style="text-align:center">PERFORMANCE</h3>

Top speed at 2000 ft.	183 mph
Cruising, 75% power at 7000 ft.	173 mph
Range Normal Lean Mixture	
Cruising, 75% power at 7000 ft.	745 mi.
92 gal., no reserve	4.3 hr.
Optimum range at 10,000 ft.	1315 mi.
128 gal., no reserve	10.7 hr.
Rate of climb sea level	
Twin engine	1340 fpm
Front engine only	355 fpm
Rear engine only	420 fpm
Service ceiling	
Twin engine	19,000 ft.
Front engine only	8200 ft.
Rear engine only	9500 ft.
Takeoff	
Ground run	625 ft.
to clear 50 ft. obstacle	1145 ft.
Landing	
Landing roll	655 ft.
to clear 50 ft. obstacle	1395 ft.

CESSNA SKYKNIGHT. Six-place, all-metal, twin-engine, supercharged, retractable-gear landplane.

SPECIFICATIONS

Engine	Two Continental 6-cylinder, fuel injection TSIO-470-B
Horsepower	260 @ 2600
Baggage	200 lbs.
Gross weight	5200 lb.
Empty weight (approx.)	3237 lb.
Fuel capacity (standard)	102 gal.
(optional)	133 gal.

PERFORMANCE

Top speed at 16,000 ft.	263 mph
Cruising, 75% power at 19,500 ft.	245 mph
Rate of climb at sea level (twin engine)	1820 fpm
(single engine)	400 fpm
Range	
Cruising, 75% power at 19,500 ft.	862 mi.
100 gal., no reserve	3.53 hr.
Optimum range at 25,000 ft.	1405 mi.
130 gal., no reserve	6.33 hr.
Service ceiling (twin engine)	28,100 ft.
(single engine)	16,600 ft.

CESSNA 205. Six-place, all-metal, fixed-gear landplane.

SPECIFICATIONS

Engine	Continental 6-cylinder fuel injection IO-470-S
Horsepower	260 @ 2625
Gross weight	3300 lb.
	1750 lb.
Fuel capacity (standard)	65 gal.
(optional)	84 gal.

PERFORMANCE

Top speed	173 mph
Cruising, 75% power at 6500 ft.	163 mph
Useful load – six 170 lb. persons, full fuel and oil plus 118 lb. extra weight allowance	
Range	
Cruising, 75% power at 6500 ft.	730 mi.
63.5 gal., no reserve	4.5 hr.
Optimum range at 10,000 ft.	1275 mi.
80 gal., no reserve	11.2 hr.
Rate of climb at sea level	965 fpm
Service ceiling	16,100 ft.

CESSNA SKYLANE. Four-place, all-metal, fixed tricycle-gear landplane.

SPECIFICATIONS

Engine	Continental O-470-R
Horsepower	230 @ 2600
Baggage	120 lb.
Gross weight	2800 lb.
Empty weight (approx.)	1635 lb.
Fuel capacity (standard)	65 gal.
(optional)	84 gal.

PERFORMANCE

Top speed at sea level	170 mph
Cruising, 75% power at 6500 ft.	162 mph
Rate of climb	980 fpm
Range	
Cruising, 75% power at 6500 ft.	695 mi.
60 gal., no reserve	4.3 hr.
Optimum range at 10,000 ft.	1215 mi.
79 gal., no reserve	10.0 hr.
Service ceiling	18,900 ft.

CESSNA 310H. Five- or six-place, all-metal, twin-engine, retractable-gear landplane.

SPECIFICATIONS

Engine	Two continental 6-cylinder fuel injection IO-470-D
Horsepower	260 @ 2625
Baggage	200 lbs.
Gross weight	5100 lb.
Empty weight	3063 lb.
Fuel capacity (standard)	102 gal.
(optional)	133 gal.

PERFORMANCE

Top speed at sea level	240 mph
Cruising, 75% power at 6500 ft.	223 mph
Rate of climb	
Twin engine (5100 lb. gross)	1690 fpm
(4700 lb. gross)	1880 fpm
Single engine (5100 lb. gross)	378 fpm
(4700 lb. gross)	475 fpm
Range	
Cruising, 75% power at 6500 ft.	780 mi.
100 gal., no reserve	3.5 hr.
Maximum range at 10,000 ft.	1300 mi.
130 gal., no reserve	7.3 hr.
Service ceiling	
Twin engine (5100 lb. gross)	21,000 ft.
(4700 lb. gross)	22,500 ft.
Single engine (5100 lb. gross)	7450 ft.
(4700 lb. gross)	9150 ft.

NOTE: Single engine service ceiling increases 425 ft. each 30 min. of flight. All performance
figures are at 5100 lb. gross weight unless otherwise indicated.

CESSNA 182. Four-place, all-metal, fixed tricycle-gear landplane.

SPECIFICATIONS

Engine	Continental O-470-R
Horsepower	230 @ 2600
Baggage	120 lb.
Gross weight	2800 lb.
Empty weight	1555 lb.
Fuel capacity (standard)	65 gal.
(optional)	84 gal.

PERFORMANCE

Top speed at sea level	167 mph
Cruising, 75% power at 6500 ft.	159 mph
Rate of climb at sea level	980 fpm
Range	
Cruising, 75% power at 6500 ft.	685 mi.
60 gal., no reserve	4.3 hr.
Optimum range, at 10,000 ft.	1190 mi.
79 gal., no reserve	10.0 hr.
Service ceiling	18,900 ft.

CESSNA 180. Four-place, all-metal, fixed-gear landplane.

SPECIFICATIONS

Engine	Continental O-470-R
Horsepower	230 @ 2600
Baggage	120 lb.
Gross weight	2650 lb.
Empty weight (approx.)	1530 lb.
Fuel capacity (standard)	65 gal.
(optional)	84 gal.

PERFORMANCE

Top speed at sea level	170 mph
Cruising, 75% power at 6500 ft.	162 mph
Rate of climb	1130 fpm
Range	
Cruising, 75% power at 6500 ft.	695 mi.
60 gal., no reserve	4.3 hr.
Optimum range at 10,000 ft.	1215 mi.
79 gal., no reserve	10.0 hr.
Service ceiling	21,500 ft.

CESSNA SKYHAWK POWERMATIC. Four-place, all-metal, fixed tricycle-gear landplane.

SPECIFICATIONS

Engine	Continental GO-300-E
Horsepower	175 @ 2400
Baggage	120 lb.
Gross weight	2500 lb.
Empty weight (approx.)	1425 lb.
Fuel capacity	52 gal.

PERFORMANCE

Top speed at sea level	148 mph
Cruising, 75% power at 7000 ft.	140 mph
Rate of climb at sea level	830 fpm
Range	
Cruising, 75% power at 7000 ft.	545 mi.
41.5 gal., no reserve	3.9 hr.
Optimum range, at 10,000 ft.	615 mi.
41.5 gal., no reserve	5.1 hr.
Service ceiling	17,000 ft.

CESSNA 172 POWERMATIC. Four-place, all-metal, fixed tricycle-gear land-plane.

SPECIFICATIONS

Engine	Continental GO-300-E
Horsepower	175 @ 2400
Baggage	120 lb.
Gross weight	2500 lb.
Empty weight (approx.)	1360 lb.
Fuel capacity	52 gal.

PERFORMANCE

Top speed at sea level	146 mph
Cruising, 75% power at 7000 ft.	138 mph
Rate of climb at sea level	830 fpm
Range	
Cruising, 75% power at 7000 ft.	540 mi.
41.5 gal., no reserve	3.9 hr.
Optimum range, at 10,000 ft.	610 mi.
41.5 gal., no reserve	5.1 hr.
Service ceiling	17,000 ft.

CESSNA SKYHAWK. Four-place, all-metal, fixed tricycle-gear landplane.

SPECIFICATIONS

Engine	Continental O-300-D
Horsepower	145 @ 2700
Baggage	120 lb.
Gross weight	2300 lb.
Empty weight (approx.)	1330 lb.
Fuel capacity	42 gal.

PERFORMANCE

Top speed at sea level	139 mph
Cruising, 75% power at 7000 ft.	131 mph
Rate of climb at sea level	645 fpm
Range	
Cruising, 75% power at 7000 ft.	600 mi.
39 gal., no reserve	4.6 hr.
Optimum range, at 10,000 ft.	720 mi.
39 gal., no reserve	7.1 hr.
Service ceiling	13,100 ft.

CESSNA 172. Four-place, all-metal, fixed tricycle-gear landplane.

SPECIFICATIONS

Engine	Continental O-300-C
Horsepower	145 @ 2700
Baggage	120 lb.
Gross weight	2300 lb.
Empty weight (approx.)	1260 lb.
Fuel capacity	42 gal.

PERFORMANCE

Top speed at sea level	138 mph
Cruising, 75% power at 7000 ft.	130 mph
Rate of climb at sea level	645 fpm
Range	
Cruising, 75% power at 7000 ft.	595 mi.
39 gal., no reserve	4.6 hr.
Optimum range, at 10,000 ft.	720 mi.
39 gal., no reserve	7.1 hr.
Service ceiling	13,100 ft.

CESSNA 210. Four-place, all-metal, retractable tricycle-gear landplane.

SPECIFICATIONS

Engine	Continental 6-cylinder fuel injection IO-470-S
Horsepower	260 @ 2625
Baggage	120 lb.
Gross weight	3000 lb.
Empty weight (approx.)	1780 lb.
Fuel capacity (standard)	65 gal.
(optional)	84 gal.

PERFORMANCE

Top speed at sea level	198 mph
Cruising, 75% power at 7000 ft.	189 mph
Rate of climb	1270 fpm
Range	
Cruising, 75% power at 7000 ft.	845 mi.
63.5 gal., no reserve	4.5 hr.
Optimum range, at 10,000 ft.	1530 mi.
80 gal., no reserve	11.2 hr.
Service ceiling	20,300 ft.

Accuracy landing. A landing in which the pilot sets, or strives to set, his aircraft down on a particular spot or place in the proper or normal gliding and landing attitude, usually following a prescribed flight path or pattern. Also called "precision landing."

Acrobatics. The performance of stunts or gymnastic feats on an aircraft in flight, such as wing-walking, trapeze-swinging, etc.

ADF. Abbreviation for Automatic Direction Finder.

Adjustable-pitch propeller. A propeller the blade angle of which may be varied only with the propeller at rest, by manually loosening locks or clamps and turning the propeller blades in their hub.

Aerobatics. The performance of stunts, such as dives, loops, steep banks, rolls, etc., in an aircraft.

Aerodynamics. The science that studies the motion of air and other gaseous fluids, and the forces acting on bodies when the bodies move through such fluids, or when such fluids move against or around the bodies.

Aeronautic chart. A map representing a portion of the earth's land area or land and water area, made especially for use in air navigation.

Aileron. A movable control surface or device, one of a pair or set located in or attached to the wings on both sides of an airplane, the primary usefulness of which is to control the airplane laterally or in roll by creating unequal or opposing lifting forces on opposite sides of the airplane.

Air current. A current or flow of air; a rising or descending current of air.

Airflow. A flow or stream of air. A relative airflow can occur, as past the wing or other parts of a moving airplane; a rate of flow, measured by mass or volume per unit of time.

Airfoil. A structure, piece or body, originally similar to a foil or leaf in being wide and thin, designed to obtain a useful reaction upon itself in its motion through the air. An airfoil may be no more than a flat plate, but usually it has a cross section carefully contoured in accordance with its intended application or function. Airfoils are applied to aircraft for sustentation (as a wing), for control (as an elevator), and for thrust or propulsion (as a propeller blade).

Airframe. The structure of an aircraft apart from accessories and power plant. The principal parts of the airframe of an airplane include the fuselage, wings, empennage, landing gear, and nacelles or pods.

Air lane. A route or way in the air, usually one provided with air-navigation aids and prescribed by proper authority.

Air marker. A mark or sign on the ground so made as to be visible to aircraft, indicating direction or giving other useful information.

Air pocket. A place in the air where conditions are such as to cause an aircraft to drop, rise, or swerve; especially a downward stream of air that causes an aircraft to drop, as into a pocket.

Airport beacon. A rotating beacon located at or near an airport to indicate the specific or general location of the airport.

Airport of entry. An airport including customs facilities, etc., through which air traffic is cleared to or from another country.

Airport Surveillance Radar (ASR). Radar equipment or a radar system used in air traffic control, which scans the airspace for a distance of approximately thirty to sixty miles around an airport and which shows, on an indicator in the airport control tower, the location of all airborne aircraft below a certain altitude and obstructions to flight within its range. Used in conjunction with Precision Approach Radar (PAR).

Air-position indicator. A flight instrument that automatically and continuously calculates and indicates the position of an aircraft.

Air route. A route or established way in the air connecting airports, regularly traveled by aircraft and usually provided with air-navigation aids and governed by flight rules.

Airspace. Space in the air above the surface of the earth, or a particular portion of such space, usually defined by the boundaries of an area on the surface, projected upward.

Airspeed. The speed of anything relative to the surrounding air; especially, the speed of an aircraft relative to the air through which it flies.

Airspeed indicator. Any instrument or meter designed to indicate airspeed; commonly, an instrument designed either to show measurements of airspeed related to assumed air conditions or to show airspeed measurements automatically corrected for certain existing air conditions.

Air temperature. The temperature of the air; specifically, the temperature of the air about a flying aircraft.

Air traffic clearance. An authorization for an aircraft to fly in an airspace within which air traffic control is exercised, under specified conditions that will prevent collision with other known aircraft within the airspace.

Air Traffic Control (ATC). The control of air traffic to maintain its safe, orderly and expeditious movement; a service or organization providing this control; the air traffic controller.

Airway. A designated air route between points on the earth's surface; specifically a civil airway.

Airway beacon. A rotating beacon located on or near an airway, other than an airport beacon or landmark beacon, serving to indicate the location of the airway. The beacon is usually provided with course lights.

Air work. Activity in the air; flying practice; that part of a flying training course in which actual flight is performed.

Airworthiness. The state or quality of an aircraft or of an aircraft component or accessory being fitted safely to perform or be used within the limitations imposed by its intended purpose or use; especially, this state or quality as certified by proper authority.

All-movable tail. A horizontal or vertical tail surface that pivots as a whole, as distinct from the usual combinations of fixed and movable surfaces. Also called a "slab tail."

Allowable load. The maximum load permissible on a structural member or part under given conditions.

Altimeter. Any of various types of instruments for measuring altitude; specifically, an instrument similar to an aneroid barometer that utilizes the change of atmospheric pressure with altitude to indicate the approximate elevation above a given point or plane used as a reference.

Altimeter setting. A pressure value used for setting a pressure altimeter so that upon landing of the aircraft at an airport the instrument will indicate an altitude equal to or very close to the field elevation above sea level.

Altitude. Height, especially height as measured above a given point, as above average sea level or above a point on the terrain; a station, position, or region at height, as to maintain altitude, or to climb to altitude.

Altitude sickness. Sickness, such as aeroembolism, brought on by ascent to high altitudes, or sickness brought on by the expansion of gas or air in the body owing to reduced external pressure at altitude.

Angle of attack. The angle at which a body, such as an airfoil or fuselage, or a system of bodies, such as a helicopter rotor, meets a flow ordinarily measured between a reference line in the body and a line in the direction of the flow or in the direction of movement of the body.

Angle of bank. The angle or roll of an aircraft, especially in making a turn.

Angle of climb. The angle between a horizontal plane and the flight path of a climbing aircraft.

Angle of crab. The horizontal angle between the longitudinal axis of a crabbed aircraft and its line of flight; a drift angle.

Approach. 1. An act or instance of bringing an aircraft in to a landing, or an aircraft coming in to a landing, including flying a landing pattern and descending; as, to begin an *approach,* or to make a landing in the first *approach.* 2. An access, way, or avenue through which aircraft are brought in to land, as, a clear *approach.* 3. The flight path or line of movement of an aircraft in an approach; as, to fly a straight *approach.*

Approach control. The supervision and direction of air traffic arriving at, departing from, and flying in the vicinity of an airdrome, under instrument flying conditions (IFR); a service or organization providing this control; the approach controller.

Approach light. Any one of a line of lights indicating the direction of approach to a runway or strip, marking the center line of a runway or water lane, etc.

Approach pattern. The flight pattern flown by an aircraft in making an approach to a landing. Also called a "landing pattern."

Apron. An area, ordinarily paved, for parking or handling aircraft.

Artificial horizon. A gyro-operated flight instrument that shows the pitching and banking attitudes of an aircraft with respect to the horizon, within limited degrees of movement, by means of the relative position of lines or marks on the face of the instrument representing the aircraft and the horizon.

Aspect ratio. The ratio of the square of the span of an airfoil to the total airfoil area, or the ratio of its span to its mean chord.

ASR. See Airport Surveillance Radar.

ATC. See Air Traffic Control.

Atmosphere. 1. The body of air surrounding the earth; also, the body of gases surrounding or comprising any planet or other celestial body. 2. A unit of pressure equal to 14.70 pounds per square inch, representing the atmospheric pressure at mean sea level under standard conditions; as, a pressure of two atmospheres.

Attitude. The position or orientation of an aircraft either in motion or at rest, as determined by the relationship between its axes and some reference line or plane or some fixed system of reference axes.

Attitude control. The control of the attitude of an aircraft, guided missile, etc.

Automatic Direction Finder. A type of radio compass which, when properly tuned to a radio transmitting station, automatically indicates the direction of the station in relation to the heading of the aircraft, without the 180° ambiguity characteristic of other types of radio compasses. The loop antenna of the automatic direction finder is rotated to the proper position for direction indicating by an electric motor operated by variations in the signal received in the loop. The automatic direction finder is sometimes called an "automatic radio compass" or "radio compass."

Automatic pilot. A device or apparatus that automatically controls the flight of an aircraft to some extent; usually a device that automatically maintains the attitude of an aircraft and steers it in a desired path.

Azimuth. Horizontal direction or bearing, as to find the *azimuth.* The horizontal direction of a celestial body with respect to a terrestrial reference direction, usually measured clockwise from a northern reference direction through 360° and so distinguished from azimuth angle and also distinguished from bearing.

Back-pressure. Pressure exerted backward; in a field of flow, a pressure exerted contrary to the pressure producing the main flow.

Back-to-chest acceleration. Accelerating force acting on the human body in the direction from back to the chest, as occurs when seated facing forward in an aircraft moving with increasing speed. It is a type of transverse acceleration.

Bank. The position or attitude of an airplane, glider, helicopter, or the like, when its lateral axis is inclined to the horizontal; as, to put an airplane into a *bank.* A *right bank* is a bank in which the lateral axis inclines downward to starboard.

Bank indicator. A flight instrument consisting of a ball enclosed in a slightly curved transparent tube filled with a damping liquid, the position of the ball in the tube being intended especially to indicate skidding or slipping in a turn. This instrument is commonly mounted in the same case with a turn indicator to make the turn-and-bank indicator.

Barometer. An instrument that measures atmospheric pressure. A barometer commonly employs for its purpose either a column of mercury in a glass tube, balanced by the pressure of the atmosphere, or a partially evacuated and scaled capsule responsive to pressure changes.

Barrel roll. An aerobatic performance in which an airplane is made to roll while simultaneously revolving about an offset axis, describing a corkscrew flight path.

Bearing. The horizontal direction of an object or point, usually measured clockwise from a reference line or direction through 360°. In navigation, bearing is used with reference to the direction of a terrestrial object or point, as distinguished from azimuth.

Biplane. An airplane having double-decked wings, one above the other. In most configurations, either the lower wing or both the lower and upper wings are divided by the fuselage.

Blackout. A condition in which vision is temporarily obscured by a blackness, accompanied by a dullness of certain of the other senses, brought on by decreased blood pressure in the head and a consequent lack of oxygen, as may occur, e.g., in pulling out of a high-speed dive in an airplane. This condition is sometimes followed by a loss of consciousness, but the unconsciousness is not usually regarded as a part of the blackout.

Blind. Flying under conditions of low visibility, using instruments, radio aids, or radar aids, as in *blind* bombing, *blind* flying; flying in which the pilot cannot see out, under either natural or simulated conditions.

Block time. The time taken by an aircraft to travel from its point of departure to its ultimate destination, measured from the moment the chocks or blocks are removed at the place of departure to the moment that they are replaced at the destination. The time spent at intermediate stops is included in the total *block time.*

Boundary light. Any one of the lights marking the limits of a landing area. Boundary lights are commonly mounted on a cone-shaped boundary marker or are set flush with the surface.

Bungee. A spring, elastic cord, or other tension device used, e.g., in a control system on an aircraft to balance an opposing force or a landing gear to assist in retracting the gear or to absorb shock, etc.

Burble. A separation or breakdown of the streamline flow past a body; the eddying or turbulent flow resulting from this.

Bush pilot. A pilot who regularly flies in wild, desolate, or relatively unsettled country, as in parts of Canada or Alaska, especially without benefit of ground navigational aids, well-prepared airfields, etc.

Cabin altitude. The simulated altitude condition in a pressurized aircraft cabin.

Calibrated airspeed. An airspeed value derived when corrections have been applied to an indicated airspeed to compensate for installation errors, instrument errors, errors in Pitot-static system, and errors induced by the attitude of the aircraft or, alternatively, an airspeed value found by applying corrections to a basic airspeed for errors in the Pitot-static system and errors induced by aircraft attitude.

Calibrated altitude. Altitude as determined by the application of corrections for static-pressure error, installation error and instrument error to the indicated altitude shown by a pressure altimeter.

Calibration card. A card that gives corrections necessary to apply to an airspeed or altitude reading or value to determine calibrated airspeed or altitude.

Camber. The curvature of the mean line of an airfoil or airfoil section from leading edge to trailing edge; the amount of this curvature, expressed as the ratio of the maximum departure of the curve, from the chord to the chord length.

CAVU. Abbreviation for Ceiling And Visibility Unlimited. Pronounced as a word and and also used as a noun or adjective, as to have *CAVU,* or as in *CAVU* weather.

Ceiling. The maximum height attainable by an aircraft under given conditions and at which it can perform effectively. An overcast of clouds, dust or the like above a given area; the height of the lower surface of a cloud overcast.

Celestial navigation. Navigation in which geographical position is found by reference to celestial bodies.

Chandelle. A performance or maneuver in which an airplane makes an abrupt, steep climbing turn using its momentum for a faster rate of climb, gaining altitude and reversing its direction of flight simultaneously.

Channel. A band of radio frequencies wide enough to allow transmission without interference from transmissions on adjacent bands.

Check list. A list carried in an airplane listing things requiring attention for different operations, such as preflight operations, takeoff, landing, etc.

Checkout. An act or instance of checking out; the test or examination made of a person or piece of equipment in a check flight.

Checkpoint. A known geographical point used to ascertain the position of an aircraft; a landmark.

Chord. A straight line intersecting or touching an airfoil profile at two points; specifically, that part of such a line between two points of intersection. This line is usually a datum line joining the leading and trailing edges of an airfoil, joining the ends of the mean line or an airfoil profile, or running along the lower surface or line of an airfoil profile, from which the ordinates and angles of the airfoil are measured.

Circle marker. A circular band or mark at the approximate center of a landing area or at the intersection of the principal runways of an airfield.

Civil airway. An airway maintained and controlled by civil authority, or one designated or approved by civil authority as suitable for domestic or foreign air commerce.

Clear-air turbulence. Turbulence that occurs in clear air and is not associated with cloud formation, such as that associated with winds at low altitudes and with the jet stream at high altitudes.

Clearance. An authorization, verbal or otherwise, to depart from an airport or airfield or to fly a given route under specified conditions; a form granting such authorization.

Climb-out. The climb made directly after takeoff.

Cloud base. The lower surface of a cloud.

Cloud deck. The upper surface of a cloud.

Cockpit check. An inspection of the instruments, etc., in the cockpit for proper functioning, usually made just prior to taking off.

Code beacon. A beacon that flashes a characteristic signal by which it may be recognized. A code beacon is used, e.g., to identify a particular airport.

Collision course. The course taken by an aircraft, which if maintained will cause it to collide with another aircraft.

Compass bearing. Bearing measured relative to compass north.

Compass course. A course measured relative to compass north.

Compass heading. A heading measured relative to compass north.

Compass north. The direction toward which the north-seeking element of a magnetic compass points. This direction may differ from magnetic north because of local disturbances or errors in the compass.

Compass rose. A circle marked in degrees, or sometimes in both directions and degrees, printed or inscribed upon a compass card, upon a chart for reference purposes, marked out upon the ground for use in compass swinging, or elsewhere displayed.

Compass swinging. The action of turning an aircraft about to different headings to determine the deviation of its compass. This may be done in the air (air swinging) or on the ground (ground swinging).

Cone of silence. An inverted cone-shape space immediately above the transmitting station of a four-course radio range in which signals are received faintly or not at all.

Contact flying. Flying in which a pilot ascertains his aircraft's attitude and finds his way from place to place by visual reference to the horizon and to landmarks.

Contour line. A line on a map or chart joining topographic points of equal elevation.

Control area. An airspace of given dimensions within which air traffic control is exercised.

Control cable. A cable for transmitting controlling movement, especially a cable for moving the control surfaces of an airplane or other aircraft, either directly or through intermediate mechanisms, or a cable connecting two or more control surfaces.

Controllable-pitch propeller. A propeller whose blade angle may be changed from the cockpit while the propeller is rotating; specifically, such a propeller whose blade angle may be changed to either of only two angles, high or low.

Control surface. A movable airfoil or surface, such as an aileron, elevator, ruddervator, flap, trim tab, etc., used to control the attitude or motion of an aircraft and to guide it through the air; specifically, one of the major surfaces used principally for guidance, as an elevator, rudder, elevon, etc.

Control-surface area. The area within the outline of a control surface exclusive of any area on that side of the hinge axis nearer the fixed surface to which the control surface is attached.

Control tower. An elevated structure or place in an airdrome from which air traffic entering and leaving the airdrome is controlled; the personnel operating this tower; as, to ask the *control tower* for landing permission.

Control zone. An airspace of specified dimensions extending upward from the surface and including one or more airdromes, within which air-traffic-control rules, in addition to those governing control areas, are in effect.

Course. A predetermined or intended route or direction to be followed, measured with respect to a geographic reference direction; a line on a chart representing a course; a course made good, a resultant direction of flight represented by a straight line on a chart connecting the point of departure with the latest fix.

Crab. Of an aircraft: to fly with the nose turned to the right or left of the line of flight, as when compensating for wind effect.

Critical altitude. Any altitude above which the performance of equipment falls off, or above which some particular danger exists, or above which some condition is encountered requiring special attention, etc., and is therefore regarded as critical.

Cross. To cross the controls; to move the controls of an airplane in a direction opposite to the usual for a given maneuver or performance; e.g., to deflect the right aileron downward while holding right rudder.

Cross bearing. A bearing crossing another bearing, as drawn on a chart, providing a fix at the point of intersection.

Cross-country flight. A flight across land away from the immediate vicinity of an airfield, usually restricted to a flight in which landing is made at a place or places other than the original point of departure.

Crosswind. A wind blowing across the line of flight of an aircraft, rocket, etc., such that its chief effect is to drive the aircraft or other flying body sideways; a wind blowing across, as across the runway.

Crosswind landing gear. A castered landing gear permitting an aircraft to land in a crabbed attitude.

Cruise control. The act or practice of operating an aircraft so as to achieve the most efficient performance on a given flight under the available conditions. Cruise control may be instituted to obtain maximum economy, endurance, speed or range or maximum efficiency at a predetermined airspeed or power setting.

Cruising airspeed. The airspeed at which an aircraft cruises. The cruising airspeed for any given aircraft changes with the purpose involved, and with the altitude, winds, load and other variables.

Cruising altitude. A given indicated pressure altitude specified for cruising or maintained in cruising.

Cuban eight. A stunt or flight maneuver in which an airplane describes an eight-shaped flight path in the vertical plane by completing about three-quarters of an inside loop, half-rolling, then repeating the procedure.

Danger area. An area in which invisible hazards to flight exist, to be flown over only by permission of the proper authority.

Dead reckoning. The estimating or determining of position by advancing an earlier known position by the application of direction and speed data.

Dead-stick. Without power, as in a *dead-stick* landing, indicating a lack of control or landing *dead-stick*. Actually the stick is not dead at all, but the term is used.

Density altitude. The altitude in a standard atmosphere corresponding to a given density actually encountered.

Design load. A specified load that a structural member or part should withstand without failing. It is determined by multiplying some particular load by an appropriate factor, usually the limit load multiplied by a factor of safety.

Deviation. The deflection of a compass needle or indicator from magnetic north as a result of local magnetic conditions.

Dihedral. The spanwise inclination of a wing or other surface, such as a stabilizer, or a part of a wing or other surface to the horizontal, or to a line or plane equivalent to the horizontal.

Directional control. Control of motion about the vertical axis; in aircraft, usually by rudder.

Directional gyro. 1. A flight instrument incorporating a gyroscope that holds its position in azimuth and so indicates angular deviation from heading. 2. A gyroscope that provides directional stability in an automatic pilot or similar mechanism.

Distance-Measuring Equipment (abbreviated *DME*). Electronic navigation equipment for finding the distance between an aircraft and a ground station by measuring the time interval between the transmission of interrogation pulses from an airborne radar and the reception of answering pulses from a transponder at the ground station.

Dive. An act or instance of an aircraft descending nose downward, its longitudinal axis remaining substantially coincident with its line of flight.

Drag. A retarding force acting upon a body in motion through a fluid, parallel to the direction of motion of the body. It is a component of the total fluid forces acting on the body.

Drift. The lateral divergence or movement of the flight path of an aircraft from the direction of its heading, measured between the heading and the track, owing primarily to the effect of a crosswind.

Drift angle. An angle measured from the heading of an aircraft to its track.

Drift correction angle. A measure of the amount of turning necessary to make the track of an aircraft coincide with its course, measured from the track to the heading.

Dual controls. The control provided by a double set of cockpit controls in an aircraft.

Dual instruction. Pilot instruction in which the student flies with the instructor and is allowed to operate the aircraft with one of the sets of dual controls.

Dynamic load. A load due to an acceleration of an aircraft, as imposed by gusts, maneuvering, or landing.

Dynamic stability. The property of a body such as an aircraft, that causes it, when disturbed from an original state of steady flight or motion, to damp the oscillations set up by restoring moments and gradually return to its original state.

Eight. A flight performance or maneuver in which an airplane describes a flight path shaped like a figure eight; the flight path so described, either in horizontal or vertical plane.

Electric tachometer. A tachometer that utilizes voltage or electrical impulses to indicate rpm.

Elevation. Height or altitude above the surface of the earth or other plane.

Elevator. A control surface, usually hinged to a horizontal stabilizer, deflected to impress a pitching moment, i.e., to make the aircraft rotate about its lateral axis. An elevator may be one of a pair, each one of the pair being situated to either side of the center line, or it may be a continuous surface running from end to end of the stabilizer.

Empennage. The assembly of stabilizing and control surfaces at the tail of an aircraft.

Empty weight. The weight of an aircraft including the weight of its power plant, trapped fuel and oil, coolant (if any), fluid in the hydraulic system, ballast normally carried, fixed equipment and furnishings, and other weight as may be defined in context.

Estimated Time of Arrival (abbreviated *ETA*). The predicted time at which an aircraft in flight will reach some point, usually its destination.

Factor of safety. The ratio of an ultimate load to some applied load, usually the probable maximum applied load.

Fan marker. A location marker that transmits a fan-shaped radiation pattern in a vertical direction.

Final approach or final. That portion or leg of an approach pattern after the last turn, in which the aircraft is in line with the runway in the landing direction and descending.

Fix. In air navigation, the position of an aircraft as determined by visual reference to the surface of the earth by celestial observations, or by electronic aids, without reference to any former position.

Fixed landing gear. A landing gear that remains fixed in position at all times.

Fixed-pitch propeller. A propeller whose blade angle cannot be changed.

Flap. A hinged, pivoted or sliding airfoil or plate, or a combination of such objects regarded as a single surface, normally located at the rear of a wing, extended or deflected for increasing lift or drag, especially at takeoff or during landing.

Flare or flare out. To descend in a smooth curve in landing, making a transition from a steep descent to a direction of flight substantially parallel to the earth.

Flat spin. A spin in which the airplane remains in a more level attitude than that of a normal spin, with centrifugal force holding the airplane away from the axis of the spin.

Flight attitude. The attitude of an aircraft in flight; technically, the attitude of an aircraft with respect to the relative wind.

Flight characteristic. A characteristic exhibited by an aircraft, or the like, in flight,
such as a tendency to stall or to yaw, an ability to remain stable at certain speeds,
etc.

Flight check. A flight made to check an aircraft or the accuracy or coverage of its
equipment or instrumentation. Also, a proficiency check in flight of a pilot or
other air crew members.

Flight path. The path made or followed in the air or in space by an aircraft, i.e., the
continuous series of positions occupied by a flying body.

Flight plan. A detailed outline or statement, written or oral, relative to a given
flight, submitted to air traffic control prior to takeoff. The flight plan contains information such as the pilot's name, type of aircraft, point of departure and destination, intended cruising altitude and true airspeed, etc.

Flight simulator. A training device or apparatus that simulates certain conditions of
actual flight or of flight operations, such as piloting.

Flight test. A test of an aircraft, an aircraft engine or other component, a system, or a
person, in or by actual flight.

Flight time. Time spent in flight or in flying operations, measured, when exactness is
required, between specified instances, as between the commencement of the takeoff
run and the end of the landing run. Also called "flying time."

Fly-by. An act or instance of flying by or over a given place on the surface; a performance, demonstration, or salute in which aircraft fly past or over, usually at
a comparatively low altitude.

Flying speed. The speed at which an aircraft flies; the speed which an aircraft must
have to provide sufficient aerodynamic lift in order to become, or to remain, airborne.

Foot-to-head acceleration. Accelerating force acting on the body in the direction of
the head; acceleration in the direction that the force is applied.

Forced landing. A landing or crash landing necessitated by some adverse circumstance,
such as mechanical failure of the aircraft, bad weather, lack of fuel, etc.

Forward slip. The movement of an aircraft in a yawed attitude and following its
original forward direction of flight.

Four-course radio range. A radio range that transmits four radio beams or courses
for the guidance of aircraft.

French landing. With an airplane having a tail skid or tail wheel, a landing in which
the tail is held off the ground as long as possible before coming to a stop.

Front. The line of intersection between a frontal surface and the earth's surface.

Frontal surface. A surface of discontinuity between two air masses of dissimilar characteristics.

Fuel consumption. The rate of engine consumption, measured, e.g., in gallons or pounds
per hour.

Fuel reserve. An amount of fuel carried in excess of that calculated to be sufficient
for a given flight.

Fuel selector. A control or valve used to select fuel from one tank or another in a
system.

Full load. The entire load sustained by an aircraft at rest or in a condition of unac-
celerated flight; the amount of this load, equivalent to the gross weight of the
aircraft.

Full rich. A fuel-air mixture setting providing the maximum amount of fuel flow.

Fuselage. The main or central structure of a heavier-than-air aircraft. The word
fuselage is applied to the main central body or structure of a fixed-wing airplane, rotary-wing airplane, or glider, but it is usually not applied to a flying-
boat hull.

Fuselage strut. A strut between the longerons or nose-to-tail skeleton of a fuselage.

Gascolator. A kind of gasoline strainer incorporating a sediment bulb.

GCA. See Ground-Controlled Approach.

Geostrophic wind. A wind resulting from a balance of pressure force (high to low pressure) and Coriolis force, mathematically calculated and considered to blow parallel to straight isobars or contour lines.

Glide. A controlled descent by a heavier-than-air aircraft under little or no engine thrust in which forward motion is maintained by gravity and vertical descent is controlled by lift forces.

Glide path. 1. The flight path of an aircraft in a glide, seen from the side. 2. In an instrument landing system, a path to be followed in the glide to a landing, as fixed by a directed radio beam; the radio beam fixing this path.

Glider. A fixed-wing aircraft specially designed to glide, or to glide and soar. This kind of aircraft ordinarily has no power plant.

Glide ratio. The ratio of the horizontal distance traveled to the vertical distance descended in a glide (as 8 miles to 1 mile).

Gliding angle or glide slope. The angle between the horizontal and the glide path of an aircraft.

Graveyard spiral. A steep, descending spiral in an airplane, involuntarily made and sometimes resulting in a crash.

Grayout. A temporary condition in which vision is hazy, restricted, or otherwise impaired, owing to insufficient oxygen.

Gross weight. The total weight of an aircraft as loaded.

Ground-Controlled Approach (abbreviated as *GCA*). 1. An approach under conditions of poor visibility in which the pilot is continuously advised from the ground by radio of his position and direction as determined by radar. 2. The equipment or system used in this approach.

Ground loop. A violent, whirling turn of an airplane while moving on the ground, usually pivoting on a wingtip.

Ground-position indicator. A flight instrument that automatically plots and indicates the position of an aircraft with respect to reference points on the ground.

Ground run. The landing run or takeoff run of an aircraft on the ground.

Ground school. A school that gives nonflying instruction in various subjects related to flying.

Ground speed. The speed of an aircraft relative to the ground, or surface of the earth. It is the same as true airspeed only if the air is stationary with respect to the earth's surface.

Gyrocompass. A compass incorporating a gyroscope whose spinning axis is parallel to the earth's axis; a directional gyro.

Gyroscope. A device consisting of a wheel having much of its mass concentrated around the rim, mounted on a spinning axis which is free to rotate about one or both of two axes perpendicular to each other and to the spinning axis.

Hammerhead stall. An exaggerated form of wing-over, in which the airplane zooms into a vertical climb, stalls and yaws simultaneously and goes into a dive from which recovery is made in a direction opposite to the original direction.

Haze. A light suspension of vapor, smoke, or other fine particles in the atmosphere, sufficient to reduce visibility.

Heading. The horizontal direction in which a craft points as it flies through the air, usually expressed as an angle measured clockwise from some reference direction to the longitudinal axis of the craft. Thus heading often does not coincide with course or track because of drift or yaw.

Head-to-seat acceleration. Acceleration force acting on the body in the direction from the head to the seat, as occurs, e.g., when seated in an airplane nosing over into a dive. Sometimes called negative acceleration.

Head wind. A wind blowing from directly ahead, on the nose of the aircraft. Its principal effect is to reduce ground speed.

Hold. To circle or fly about in a particular pattern near a specified point while waiting for permission or instructions to land or to proceed along a course.

Holding point. A specified point near which an aircraft holds, flying its holding pattern. Also called a "holding fix."

Hood. An opaque screen fitted around a cockpit, or cabin, or a hood worn over the pilot's eyes so that the pilot cannot see out. It is used for training in blind flying.

Horizontal stabilizer. A stabilizer mounted more or less horizontally on an airplane affording longitudinal stability, and to which the elevators, when present, are attached.

Hypoxia. A deprivation of oxygen, especially a deprivation of oxygen extensive enough to cause impairment of the physical faculties.

Icing. The action or process by which atmospheric moisture is deposited as ice.

IFR. Abbreviation for Instrument Flight Rules.

ILS. Abbreviation for Instrument Landing System.

Indicator. An instrument, especially that part of an instrument or system that displays its measurements or indications, such as an air-position indicator, an airspeed indicator, a rate-of-climb indicator, etc.

Initial approach. In an instrument landing, the approach or holding pattern flown by an aircraft preparatory to the final approach.

Instrument approach. An approach during which the pilot is dependent entirely upon instruments and ground-based electronic and communication systems for orientation, position, altitude, etc.

Instrument flying. Flying using instruments to determine position, orientation, etc., legally required under conditions of limited visibility.

Instrument landing system. A radio-guidance and communication system designed to guide aircraft through approaches, letdowns, and landings under conditions of little or no visibility. This system consists essentially of directional radio transmitters establishing the angle of the glide path and indicating the direction of the runway, and of radio marker beacons establishing locations along the approach path.

Instrument rating. A rating authorizing a pilot to do instrument flying.

Isobaric surface. An atmospheric surface at which the pressure is the same throughout.

Joy stick. Slang. The control stick of a fixed-wing airplane.

Kickback. A reversal of engine rotation during starting caused by highly advanced timing or by preignition.

Knot. One nautical mile per hour.

Lag. A hesitation or delay, as the delay in an instrument or instrument system in indicating a change.

Landing angle. The angle between wing chord of an airplane and the horizontal at the instant of touchdown with the airplane in its normal landing attitude. In effect, the plane's angle of descent as it lands.

Landing gear. The apparatus comprising those components of an aircraft that support and provide mobility for the aircraft on land, water or other surfaces.

Landing light. A light, usually one of two or more mounted on an aircraft's wings or nose and used to light up the runway surface during landing.

Landing roll or run. The movement or travel of an aircraft under the impetus of its landing speed after touchdown.

Landing speed. The minimum speed at which an airplane may touch down under control.

Landmark beacon. A light beacon, other than an airport or airway beacon, that marks a specific geographical location.

Lapse rate. The rate of change of temperature, pressure or some other meteorological phenomenon with altitude, usually the rate of decrease of temperature with increasing height.

Lateral axis. An axis going from side to side of an aircraft, usually the side-to-side body axis passing through the center of gravity. Sometimes called a "transverse axis."

Lateral control. Control over the rolling movement of an aircraft. With a fixed-wing airplane, this control is usually accomplished by use of ailerons.

Leading edge. The forward edge of an airfoil, blade, etc.; i.e., the edge that normally meets the air first.

Lean. As in a lean or thin gas to air mixture. Having a relatively low proportion of fuel to air (leaning-out the engine).

Leg. 1. A distinct segment, as between landings, of an air journey, as the *leg* between Seattle and Anchorage. 2. One of the straight-line segments of a pattern flown in the air, as a crosswind *leg*.

Letdown. The act of letting down, especially the gliding descent of an aircraft from cruising altitude prior to an approach or landing.

Level. To level off or out. To enter horizontal flight after a climb, dive or glide.

Lift. That component of the total aerodynamic force acting on a body perpendicular to the direction of the undisturbed airflow relative to the body. Sometimes called "aerodynamic lift," it acts on any body or system of bodies such as an airfoil, fuselage, or an airplane at a suitable angle of attack in the airflow.

Lift-drag ratio. The ratio of lift to drag obtained by dividing the lift by the drag, or the lift coefficient by the drag coefficient.

Limit load. The maximum load which it is calculated that an aircraft member or part will experience in service.

Link trainer. A simulator for training in certain skills or techniques, especially instrument flying.

Load. That which is put or intended to be put, aboard an aircraft.

Localizer. A radio beacon used in an instrument landing system to give lateral guidance along the final approach. The localizer transmits two signal patterns overlapping along the center line of the runway and along the projection of the center line from both ends of the runway.

Location marker. Any of several kinds of radio beacons located along an airway or in an instrument landing system, transmitting a characteristic signal to provide position or distance information to aircraft.

Log. A record of flight by an aircraft, containing information such as that concerning the course or courses flown, speed, positions, important occurrences aboard the aircraft; or a history of a particular piece of equipment, as of an engine; or a record of a pilot's flying hours, including kind of flying performed.

Longitudinal axis. An axis going from nose to tail of an aircraft, usually a fore-and-aft body axis passing through the center of gravity.

Loop. A maneuver in which the airplane makes an approximately circular flight path in the vertical plane, its lateral axis remaining horizontal and perpendicular to the flight path.

Loop antenna. A directional antenna in the form of a closed loop, rectangle or other shape.

Loop-type radio range. A type employing two loop antennas placed at right angles to each other. One antenna sends out the Morse letter "A" and the other sends out the letter "N," producing a radiation pattern resembling in a graphic representation two figure eights crossing one another containing four overlapping zones or quadrants with alternating "A" and "N" zones. Commonly called low frequency radio (LF).

Magnetic bearing. Bearing measured relative to magnetic north.

Magnetic compass. A compass that uses a pivoted magnetic needle or some other magnetic sensing element that aligns itself with the Earth's magnetic lines of force to indicate direction.

Magnetic course. A course measured relative to magnetic north.

Magnetic heading. Heading measured relative to magnetic north.

Magnetic north. The direction north as indicated by a magnetic compass influenced only by the Earth's magnetic field.

Magneto (in shortened form, "mag"). A type of electric generator using permanent magnets to supply an electric current for engine ignition.

Manifold-pressure gauge. A gauge that measures manifold absolute pressure of the engine, measured from zero and expressed in inches of mercury.

Middle marker. In an instrument landing system, a fan marker near the approach end of a runway.

Minimal flight path. The flight path between two points that marks the shortest possible time en route.

Minimum. The lowest condition or limit of ceiling, visibility, altitude, etc., at which flight operation is permitted.

Mixture control. A carburetor control for adjusting the fuel-air ratio.

Mush. To settle or to gain little or no altitude while flying in a semistalled condition or at a high angle of attack.

Nautical mile. A unit of distance equal to one minute of a great circle.

Navigable airspace. Airspace above certain minimum safe altitudes prescribed by proper authority, in which air navigation is permissible.

Navigation. The art or science of guiding aircraft, etc., from place to place, including determining position and distance traveled and making use of any of several different methods or combinations of methods, involving geometrical calculations, reference to celestial bodies, reference to landmarks, radio aids or other navigational aids.

Nondirectional. Of a radio beacon, a signal, etc.: not directional; omnidirectional.

Omnidirectional radio range or omnirange (popularly, *omni*). A type of radio range that gives bearings in all directions from the transmitter.

Operations. The center at a major airport or Air Force base that controls and directs flying operations.

Outer marker. In an instrument landing system, the outermost location marker from the end of the runway.

Overcontrol. To displace or move an aircraft's controls more than is necessary for the desired performance.

Override. To supplant or neutralize the operation or effect of an automatic control, especially by a manually operated control.

Pancake. To put into, or to make, a pancake landing, in which the airplane is leveled off and stalled rather high above the surface, as a result of which the airplane settles rapidly on a steep flight path and strikes the surface forcefully.

Panel. A board of some kind holding controls or instruments; or a section of an airplane wing.

Pants. A set of teardrop-shaped fairings around the wheels of a fixed landing gear.

PAR. See Precision Approach Radar.

Pass. A short, brief run or movement of an aircraft in its flight over a target or over an intended landing area.

Path. A line of movement or a way, e.g., a flight *path*.

Pattern. The horizontal configuration or form of the flight path flown by an aircraft, near an airport as it approaches for a landing or leaves the field after a takeoff.

Pilotage. Air navigation by visual reference to landmarks, especially with the aid of maps or charts. Also called "piloting."

Pilot certificate. Issued by the Federal Aviation Agency, granting a person authorization to operate aircraft to an extent limited by the type of certificate and the rating of the holder.

Pitch axis. A lateral axis through an aircraft about which the body pitches.

Pitot tube. An open-ended tube or tube arrangement which, when immersed in a moving fluid with the mouth pointed upstream, may be used to measure the stagnation pressure of the fluid. It is used in measuring airspeed.

Placard. A posted notice on or in an aircraft setting forth a requirement or limiting condition in operation.

Position. The location of an aircraft with respect to geographical coordinates, a city, a topographical feature, etc.

Position report. A report from an aircraft in flight to a controlling station giving the aircraft's position, often together with other information, such as heading, speed, etc.

Power approach. A landing approach during which the airplane is under power to provide better control.

Power dive. A dive in an airplane, especially a steep dive, under considerable or full power.

Power landing. A landing in which the airplane is under power until it touches down.

Power setting. The setting of any control or regulator that affects the output of an engine or power plant, such as a throttle setting, a mixture-control setting, or a propeller-pitch setting.

Precision Approach Radar (PAR). Radar equipment or a radar system used in an airport traffic control system, that displays on radar screens in the airport control tower, highly accurate indications of the range, azimuth and elevation of aircraft on approach to a landing.

Preflight. Before a flight, as in *preflight* planning; or pertaining to activities preceding training, as in *preflight* school.

Prime. To introduce fuel into the induction system or cylinders of an engine before starting as an aid to firing the engine.

Propeller hub. The central portion or part of a propeller, often containing a pitch-changing mechanism, from which the blades radiate and by means of which the propeller is mounted on its drive shaft.

Pylon. A post or towerlike structure used as a course marker or as a ground reference for precision maneuvers; for example in a pylon eight manuever.

Quadrant. Any one of the four signal zones in a four-course radio range.

Quartering wind. A wind moving in a direction that makes an angle of approximately 45° with the longitudinal axis of an aircraft.

Radar. A method of using beamed, reflected and timed radio waves for detecting, locating, or tracking objects, for measuring altitude, etc., in any of various activities such as air traffic control, guidance or gunnery.

Radial. Any one of the bearing lines radiating from an omnidirectional radio range.

Radio aid. Any navigation aid utilizing radio, such as a radio beacon, radio compass, etc.

Radio Compass. A direction-indicating, radio-receiving apparatus used aboard aircraft, which makes use of the directional characteristics of a loop antenna for finding and indicating direction in relation to a radio-transmitting station to which the receiver is tuned.

Radio direction-finder. A radio-receiving set, together with its associated equipment, used to determine the direction from which a radio signal is transmitted.

Radio navigation. Navigation by means of radio aids or navigation systems using radio, as by the radio compass, radio direction-finding systems, etc.

Rate climb. A climb at a constant rate. Rate of climb.

Rate descent. A descent at a constant rate. Rate of descent.

Rate-of-climb indicator. A flight instrument that indicates the rate of climb or rate of descent of an aircraft in any convenient unit, e.g., feet per minute.

Rate-of-turn indicator. An instrument marked to indicate by needle, the rate at which the plane is turning.

Read. To hear clearly or understand. Used in radio ("do you read me?").

Reciprocating engine. An engine, especially an internal-combustion engine, in which a piston or pistons moving back and forth work upon a crankshaft or other device to create rotational movement.

Recovery. In flying, the action of an aircraft returning, or being restored, to its initial attitude after a spin, dive, loop, roll, etc.

Reporting point. A geographic location in relation to which the position of an aircraft is reported, or is to be reported.

Reversible-pitch propeller. A propeller whose pitch may be changed to negative angle so as to give reverse thrust, used for braking action.

Rhumb line. A line of constant direction that intersects all meridians at the same angle. A rhumb line appears as a straight line on a Mercator projection.

Rich. Having a relatively high proportion of fuel to air.

Rime or rime ice. An opaque white ice of granular structure, less dense than glaze ice.

Roll. To rotate about the plane's longitudinal axis.

Roll-out. The act of making a landing roll, or the act of recovering from a banked attitude.

Rotating beacon. A light beacon that rotates about a vertical axis on planes, at airports, and on airways. Aircraft beacons are red; airports green and white.

Round-out. A flare out, especially that part of the flare out near the surface.

Rudder. An upright control surface that is deflected to impress a yawing moment, i.e., to make the aircraft rotate about its vertical axis.

Rudder pedal. Either one of a pair of cockpit pedals for operating a rudder or other direction-control device.

Run-up. An act or instance of running an engine up, in order to test or warm the engine or to examine it for proper operation.

Runway light. Any one of a line of lights along either side of a runway to mark its location at night.

Safety belt. A restraining belt fastened about a person's body to prevent his being thrown about under sudden or abnormal acceleration.

Safety pilot. A pilot who accompanies a student pilot or a pilot practicing hooded flight to warn of danger or to take over the controls if need be.

Seat-to-head acceleration. Accelerating force acting on the body in the direction from the seat to the head, as occurs when seated in an airplane pulling out of a dive. Sometimes called "positive acceleration."

Selector valve. A valve used to direct the flow of a fluid to a particular mechanism, as in a hydraulic system.

Sequence valve. An automatic valve in a hydraulic system that causes one hydraulic action to follow another in a definite order.

Service ceiling. The height above sea level, under standard air conditions, at which a given airplane is unable to climb faster than a specified rate.

Shoulder harness. A harness that fastens over a person's shoulders to prevent his being thrown forward in his seat.

Sideslip. A sideways movement of an aircraft to one side or the other of the projected initial flight path.

Simulator. A device, such as a Link trainer, an electronic apparatus, that simulates flight or some other condition in one way or another.

Sink. To descend; to descend in a glide.

Skid. A sideways movement of an aircraft toward the outside of its turn.

Slab tail. Same as all-movable tail.

Slip. A sideways movement of an aircraft in flight.

Slipstream. The stream of air driven backward by a rotating propeller. The airstream past an aircraft.

Slow roll. A roll performed largely by movement of the ailerons, the rudder and elevators being used for trimming purposes, and the flight path remaining substantially straight throughout.

Snap roll. The airplane is first brought sharply nose-up, then rolled by a quick application of the rudder in the desired direction of roll. Essentially a spin executed in horizontal flight.

Solo flight. A flight in which the pilot is alone in the aircraft.

Span. The dimensions of an airplane, measured from wingtip to wingtip. The dimension of an airfoil from tip to tip, measured in a straight line.

Spin. A maneuver of an airplane, controlled or uncontrolled, in which the airplane descends in a corkscrew path while flying at an angle of attack greater than the angle of maximum lift.

Spiral. A maneuver of an airplane in which the craft ascends or descends in a corkscrew path, distinguished from a spin in that the angle of attack is within the normal range of flight angles.

Spot landing. An airplane landing in which the pilot attempts to make initial contact with the ground by landing at a preselected spot. Same as an accuracy landing.

Stabilizer. A fixed or adjustable airfoil or vane that provides stability for an aircraft, specifically the horizontal stabilizer on a plane.

Stall. A condition in which the wing flies at an angle of attack greater than the angle of its maximum lift, resulting in a loss of lift and an increase of drag, causing the plane to lose altitude.

Stalling angle. The minimum angle of attack of an airfoil at which a stall will occur.

Stalling speed. The airspeed at which, under a given set of conditions, an aircraft will stall.

Standard rate turn. A turn in an aircraft in which the heading changes at the rate of 3° per second.

Static tube. A tube provided with one or more openings that are presented to the fluid so that the stream flows across them. A static tube is combined with a Pitot tube in the Pitot-static tube to measure airspeed.

Strut. A supporting brace, as in a fuselage between the longerons, or in a landing gear to transmit the airplane loads, etc.

Sweep. The slant of a wing or other airfoil or of a reference line in an airfoil, with respect to a plane perpendicular to the longitudinal axis.

Tab. A small auxiliary airfoil let into the trailing edge of an aircraft control surface and used for trim, or to move or assist in moving, the larger surface.

Tachometer (popularly, "tach"). An instrument that indicates, usually in revolutions per minute, the rotational speed of an engine.

Tail section. The rear section or portion of a fuselage, hull, or other body, usually understood to include the tail assembly.

Tail wind. A wind blowing from directly behind, or blowing from such a direction that its principal effect is to increase ground speed.

Takeoff distance. The distance required for the takeoff run of an aircraft under given conditions.

Takeoff run or roll. Travel or movement between the point of accelerating for the takeoff and the point at which the plane becomes airborne.

Takeoff speed. The airspeed at which an aircraft becomes airborne under given conditions.

Takeoff time. The time for which a takeoff is scheduled, or at which a takeoff occurred.

Taxi. To move about on the ground, water or other surface under the craft's own power, except in takeoff and landing runs.

Tetrahedron. An object having four sides; in aviation, used on airports as a wind-direction and runway indicator.

Three-point landing. With conventional-gear airplanes, a landing in which the two main wheels and the tail wheel or tail skid, touch the surface simultaneously.

Timed turn. A turn at a constant rate of change in heading held for a specific interval of time.

To-from indicator. An aircraft radio needle showing if the plane is heading to or from a radio range.

Touch-and-go landing. A landing in which the aircraft touches down, and takes off again without coming to a full stop.

Touchdown. To make contact between the landing gear and the landing surface, either with or without completing the landing run and coming to a stop or rest.

Track. The path or actual line of movement of an aircraft over the surface of the earth.

Traffic pattern. A prescribed pattern to be followed by aircraft in the air about an airport.

Tricycle landing gear. A landing gear comprising two wheels or sets of main landing gear in line and a nose wheel unit.

Trim. The condition of an airplane in which it maintains a fixed attitude with respect to the wind axes, the moments about the aircraft's axes being in equilibrium.

Trim tab. A tab that is deflected to a position where it remains to keep the aircraft in desired trim.

True airspeed. Actual or exact airspeed.

True-airspeed indicator. An airspeed indicator designed to show acceptable values of true airspeed; an airspeed indicator that automatically compensates for varying conditions.

True altitude. Altitude above mean sea level.

True bearing. Bearing measured relative to true north.

True course. A course measured relative to true north.

True heading. Heading measured relative to true north.

True north. The direction of the geographic North Pole.

Turbulence. An agitated condition of the air; a disordered, irregular, mixing motion of the air over the earth.

Turn. An act of changing horizontal direction, usually by maneuver in a substantially horizontal plane.

Turn-and-bank indicator. A flight instrument that combines a bank indicator and a turn indicator in the same housing.

Undershoot. To fall short of intended mark of landing touchdown.

Unidirectional. That goes or transmits in one direction only.

Vapor lock. A stoppage or diminution of fuel flow in a system caused by fuel vapor in the lines.

Venturi tube. A converging-diverging passage for fluid, which increases the fluid velocity and lowers its pressure. It has various applications, such as for driving suction-operated aircraft instruments. It has also been used in airspeed indicators.

Vertical axis. An axis passing through an aircraft from top to bottom and usually passing through the center of gravity.

Vertical bank. An incline in which the lateral axis of the aircraft is perpendicular, or substantially so, to the horizontal plane.

VFR. See Visual Flight Rules.

Visibility. The range of vision within which prominent objects can be distinguished; in determining and reporting weather conditions, the horizontal distance to which good vision is possible.

Visual flight. Flight in which the pilot uses his vision directly, rather than instruments, to determine attitude, position with respect to other objects, etc.

Visual Flight Rules (abbreviated as *VFR*). Rules specified by a qualified authority, establishing minimum flying altitudes and limits of visibility to govern visual flight. A minimum of 3 miles forward visibility and 1000 ft. ceiling over most areas.

Warm-up. The act of warming an engine up.

Whip stall. A stall which the airplane first goes into in a steep nose-up attitude, then turns sharply or "whips" into a steep nose-down attitude. Sometimes performed intentionally.

Wind direction. The direction from which a wind blows.

Wind drift. Drift caused by wind.

Winds aloft. Winds at high altitudes, unaffected by surface features; the direction and speed of such winds.

Wind sock. A fabric sleeve mounted so as to catch and swing with the wind, thus showing the wind direction; also shows wind force.

Wind tee. A weather vane shaped like the letter T, located on a landing area to show the wind direction to flying aircraft. Also called a landing tee.

X-axis. A designation for the longitudinal axis in a coordinate system.

Yaw. The rotational or oscillatory movement of an aircraft about a vertical axis.

Y-axis. A designation for the lateral axis in a coordinate system.

Z-axis. A designation for the vertical axis in a coordinate system.

Zero-zero. A condition such that there is no effective visibility in either a horizontal or a vertical direction.

Zoom. A brief, steep climb of an airplane, the airplane's momentum being expended in the climb.

INDEX

Electric tachometer, 232
Electrical shorts, 31, 34
Electrical system, 17, 32, 34, 44–45, 237
Elevation, defined, 232
Elevators, 101, 232
   checking, 34, 38, 39, 45
   function of, 24–26, 232
   positions of, illustrated, 25
Empennage, 232
Empty weight, 232
Engine, 20, 21, 24, 31, 32, 34
   failure of, 29, 47
   make of. *See* specific planes
   mixture control settings for, 41
   reciprocating, 239
   pre-flight check of, 34, 37, 40, 44, 45
   RPM gauge for, 33
   run-up of, 17, 31, 44–45, 81, 239
   spirals and, 96
Engine mounts, checking, 34
Ercoupe, 184
Estimated Time of Arrival (ETA), 123, 232
Estimated Time of Departure (ETD), 123
ETA (Estimated Time of Arrival), 123, 232
ETD (ESTIMATED Time of Departure), 123

FAA. *See* Federal Aviation Agency
Factor of safety, 232
Facts of Flight (pamphlet), 146
Fan marker, 232
Fear, of flying, 56, 72
   of getting lost, 111, 134, 135
   of landing, 84–85
Federal Aviation Agency (FAA), 48, 74, 102, 108
   annual inspection by, 173
   attempts to standardize equipment, 31, 98
   cross-country flight requirements, 110, 133
   flight instruction and, 94, 167, 168
   instrument training and, 167, 168
   landing rules, 82
   Omni-Range stations of. *See* Omni-Range radio
   private license tests. *See* License, private pilot's
   regulations, 141
   weather reports, 122–24
Field altitude, 16, 32, 42, 58, 74, 76
Fields, airplane. *See* Airports
Fighter planes, 30
Figure eight turns, 95, 232

Final approach, 19, 73, 78, 88, 100
   defined, 232
Fire, protection from, 31
Five controls of airplane, 24–29
Fix, defined, 232
Fixed landing gear, 232
Fixed-pitch propeller, 232
Flap speed, 101
Flaps, 101, 102, 232
   checking, 31, 38, 45
   function of, 24, 28–29, 44, 232
   landing and, 55, 87–88
Flare out, 55, 89, 102
   defined, 232
Flat spin, 232
Flight altitude, defined, 233
Flight check, defined, 232
Flight Following Service, VFR, 124
Flight Information Manual, 145, 147
Flight jackets, 14
Flight path, 233
Flight plan, 75, 233
Flight Service Stations (FSS), 124
Flight simulator, 233
Flight test, 149–54, 233
Flight Test Guide for the Private Pilots Examination, 168
Fly-by, 233
Flying, fundamentals of, 56–73
   instruction and instructors, 14–19, 46–55, 56–73, 93ff., 103ff., 110ff., 167–71
   mechanics of, 20–45
   reasons for, 13–14
Flying speed, defined, 233
Fog, 126
   See also Weather
Foot-to-head acceleration, 233
Forced landings, 93, 233
Forces of flight, 21–23
Forecasts, weather, 122–32
Four-course radio range, 233
Four forces of flight, 21–23
Forward slip, 233
Fowler's Guide, 146
Fractocumulus clouds, 126
Fractostratus clouds, 126
Freezing conditions, carburetor heat setting for, 41
   See also Icing
French landing, defined, 233
Frequencies, radio. *See* Radio
Frontal surface, defined, 233
Fronts, 131–32, 141–42, 233
FSS (Flight Service Stations), 124